GENERAL BIOLOGY I
LAB MANUAL Second Edition

D0435391

Jose Alberte

Thomas Pitzer

Kristy Calero

FLORIDA INTERNATIONAL UNIVERSITY

With first edition contributions from
Anna Goldina
Tanya M Simms

Mc
Graw
Hill
Education

22 23 24 25 26 27 QVS/QVS 23 22 21 20 19

ISBN-13: 978-1-259-15884-1
ISBN-10: 1-259-15884-5

Solutions Program Manager: Tricia Wagner
Project Manager: Jennifer Bartell

Contents

Acknowledgements

The authors wish to acknowledge all those who have assisted in the production of this lab text. We are especially grateful to our team of instructors and staff that over the years have given us great feedback and have made it fun to teach. A special thanks is due to Alberto Cruz whose feedback and contributions to the editing of this book made the publishing of this manual possible.

Laboratory Safety Rules

DEPARTMENT OF BIOLOGICAL SCIENCES

1. Act in a responsible manner, concentrate and work cautiously at all times.
2. Follow all safety rules and instructions posted in the classroom and those provided by your instructor.
3. Use good housekeeping practices in the lab. Keep your working area clean and uncluttered. Clean up after yourself.
4. Know how to get help in an emergency.
   - Phones are located next to the door.
   - For emergencies requiring immediate attention, dial 5911.
   - The nearest full treatment hospital is Kendal Regional Medical Center (305-223-3000).
   - For less dire emergencies, there is a list of names and numbers in each lab.
   - Lab instructors are responsible for knowing and relaying this information to students.
5. Know the location of all emergency equipment, including eye washes, fire extinguishers, showers, first aid kits, spill clean-up kits, and emergency gas shut-off switch.
6. Wear protective clothing at all times.
   - Wear safety goggles and gloves when instructed
   - **Wear lab coats at all times**
   - Do not wear clothes that restrict motion
     - Avoid "hanging" clothing that might be caught in flame or equipment.
     - Avoid miniskirts, tank-tops, sandals, etc. which increase your risk of exposure to chemicals
     - Wear clothes that can get dirty
   - **DO NOT wear open toe shoes**
   - Tie back long hair.
7. **There is absolutely no**: smoking, eating, drinking, and applying cosmetics in the laboratory.
8. Use proper pipetting devices. DO NOT suction with your mouth.
9. Wash your hands frequently, especially before leaving the laboratory, taking snack breaks, or using the toilet.
10. Never work alone in the laboratory.
11. You will be using special safety equipment, such as fume hoods and biohazard containers for certain exercises. It is absolutely necessary that you utilize special safety precautions for these labs.
12. Never attempt to identify any chemical or substance by smelling, touching, or tasting the material.
13. Report all spills immediately to the instructors who will determine the nature of the spill and its handling. Any spills beyond the control of the instructor or other qualified persons should be referred to Environmental Health and Safety (X2626) during regular hours, or Public Safety (X5911) after hours.
14. Be very careful when dispensing acids and bases. Avoid getting them on your hands or clothing. If a spill occurs, rinse the affected area thoroughly with running water.

15. Check with your instructor regarding chemical or substance disposal for every different material you use. Instructors are responsible for knowing the proper disposal of all materials used in lab.

Material	Disposal location
Trash	Trash can
Organic material and animal parts	Biohazard bags
Broken glass	Glass disposal box

16. Report broken or missing equipment to your instructor so a replacement may be obtained.
17. Clean and dry all glassware and equipment at the end of each lab section, before leaving the lab.
18. Never take chemicals, substances, or materials out of the laboratory without the knowledge and consent of the instructor.
19. If you witness an unsafe act, condition, or accident, please report this to your instructor.
20. If you have a question, ask before you act.

Microscope Rules

1. Remove microscopes from the cabinet carefully, with both hands. Carry the microscope with one around the arm, and the other supporting the base. To avoid dropping or slamming the microscope, never attempt to carry more than one scope at a time. Gently place the scope on the counter.

2. Use the microscope corresponding to your station number, and return it to the proper slot within the cabinet. The instructors will check all scopes at the end of each lab.

3. Minimize the use of eye make-up when using microscopes. These materials become deposited on ocular lenses and result in unclear images.

4. Do no use coarse adjustment with the 40X objective. Always focus by increasing the distance between the slide and the objective lens. These two basic rules prevent damage to slides and lenses.

5. Do not leave slides on the stage when the scope is put away.

6. Unplug the microscope light by grasping the plug, not the cord. Coil the cord in your hand and then place it over the upper ocular tube.

7. Before putting away the microscope make sure that:
   - The light switch is in the off position.
   - The scanning objective (4x), the low magnification objective, is in viewing position
   - Lower the position of the stage, using the coarse adjustment knob, as close to the base as possible.
   - The cord should be wrapped around the microscope.
   - There are no slides on the stage
   - The microscope is put back at its corresponding station number within the cabinet.

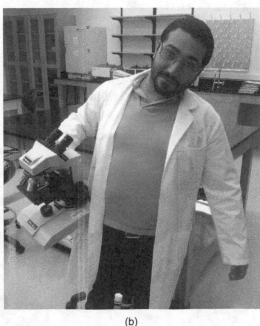

(a)   (b)

Figure 1

The proper (*a*) and improper (*b*) way to carry a microscope.

The Scientific Method

1

Objectives

- Students will familiarize themselves with lab policies and practices.
- Students will know where all emergency/safety equipment are and why they are needed in the lab setting.
- Students will identify, understand, and apply the elements of a scientific experimental plan.
- Students will determine what types of statistics are needed to make appropriate conclusions at the end of an experiment.
- Students will interpret data and make conclusions about the results of the experiment.
- Students will be able to construct a graph using Microsoft Excel.

Task 1—SAFETY: Learn About Safety in a Biology Laboratory

Introductory Notes

All tasks in this laboratory manual are designed to have students work as a team to accomplish the learning objectives. Students must come in to each laboratory session having thoroughly read the laboratory exercise(s) of the day. The instructor will provide directions or demonstrate procedures in the lab prior to the start of the any experiment. Students are encouraged to ask questions about the experiments. Always make note of any additional safety requirements before the start of any experiment. When in doubt ask!

Safety Procedure

1. Review the laboratory safety procedures with your instructor.
2. Note the location and give a brief explanation of the use and importance of each of the following safety and emergency equipment/items:
   - Shower:

   - Eyewash:

   - Medical emergency procedure/contacts:

   - Fire extinguisher:

   - First Aid Kit:

- Emergency gas cut-off valve:

- Spill kits:

- Fume Hood:

- Emergency Phone:

- AED:

Task 2—THE SCIENTIFIC METHOD

The term science refers to the body of knowledge gained through the process of systematic study. We use the process of science to discover novel and fascinating pieces of knowledge. The scientific method enables us to make observations, pose questions, and solve problems about the natural world that can be effectively and efficiently tested through repeated and unbiased experiments. It is an approach to solving problems of all types that is practical, reliable, and logical; with the ultimate goal of obtaining new knowledge.

The origin of the modern scientific method (Figure 1.1) can be traced back to the works of the Greek philosopher Aristotle, where principles of the natural world must be extrapolated from the collection and studies of observations. We all make observations of the world around us, but when dealing with science the key is to formulate informative observations that look for repeated or unusual patterns. The majority of scientific works come from trying to understand these patterns. In fact, many great scientific discoveries stem from observations of unusual events that were not expected. These patterns are crucial to creating informative and insightful observations. For example, consider the following observations: (1) All the plants I try to grow on the right side of my backyard ultimately die. (2) Despite the fact that throughout the rest of my backyard the plants prosper, the plants on the less shaded right side of my backyard ultimately yellow and die. Both statements may be true, but it is the latter of the two statements that informs us of relevant features and potential relationships. By utilizing informative observations of the natural world or by reading the works of others who have reported their observations and conclusions, a scientist can then ask questions based on this preliminary information.

Questions are the basis of our thinking processes. These questions, when using the scientific method, should be based on informative observations and lead you to a proper scientific hypothesis and suggests a pathway for investigation. The better the quality of the preliminary observations the better the quality of the questions and ultimately the hypotheses proposed. Initially questions tend to be too general, which is not necessarily a bad thing. For example, "Under what conditions do enzymes work optimally?" This might be the question we want to ultimately understand, but within the context of a scientific experiment the question is too vague. Proper questions for the process of science need to be specific enough to be answered clearly through experimentation. For example, "What pH and temperature does amylase work optimally?" Typically questions at this stage still need to be refined and further classified to lead to a more specific scientific hypothesis. For example, "Does amylase catabolize starch optimally in higher, lower, or neutral pH?" This question clearly refers to a testing subject (organism, biomolecule, etc.), variables, and processes. If at this point a clear question cannot be written, then the observations need to be reevaluated. It is very difficult to write good questions without having a proper understanding of the subject at hand first.

A hypothesis is a candidate explanation for an observed phenomenon. This explanation must be stated in a testable and falsifiable manner. This statement, also, must not be anthropomorphized. A scientific hypothesis clearly states the relationship between scientific variables and must provide a mechanistic explanation for the relationship that is being systematically tested. For example, when determining the relationship between precipitation and secondary succession an appropriate scientific hypothesis would be: Heavy precipitation during the rainy season in South Florida increases the amount of woody and herbaceous fuels, eliminating the constraints on natural brush fires, which result in secondary succession.

This statement is not to be confused with statistical hypotheses nor predictions. The purpose of statistical hypotheses is to identify or clarify patterns typically through the use of quantitative statistical data analysis. A good statistical hypothesis identifies two general components (1) the relationship between the tested variables and (2) the process(es), molecule(s) or

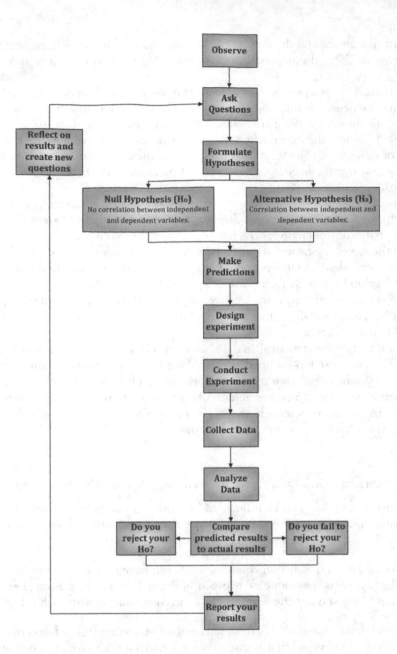

Figure 1.1

The Scientific Method.

organism(s) under scrutiny. Experimentation and its resultant data analysis is used to determine whether the statistical hypothesis should be rejected or not. There are two types of statistical hypotheses when performing statistical analysis in experiments on the natural world (1) Null Hypothesis (H_o) and (2) Alternative Hypothesis (H_a). The null hypothesis states that there is no significant determined relationship between two observed phenomena (variables). The alternative hypothesis states that there is a significant determined relationship between two observed phenomena.

These statistical hypotheses are considered concurrently when performing data analyses. Just like a scientific hypothesis the statistical hypothesis must be written in a way that it can be falsifiable. As a rule these hypotheses are not accepted as an absolute truth, but are considered to be tentatively not rejected. With that in mind, one can reject or fail to reject a statistical hypothesis in an experiment. This is the case because there remains the possibility of another experiment proving the relationship written in the statement false. It is only the hypotheses that stand the test of time and cannot be determined false through repeated experimentation which are then deemed theories (ie. Theory of Evolution, Theory of Gravity, etc.).

Once the hypotheses have been stated the next step is to make appropriate predictions. A prediction is a statement that foretells what is believed to most likely occur, based on observations. This is not to be confused with a hypothesis. A prediction does not provide a possible mechanistic explanation to the relationship depicted in the statement. Instead, it simply provides a statement that anticipates the outcome of an experiment in the lab or in nature. Statements like, "I need to buy ice cream, so I will go directly to the freezers instead of searching through the entire store," are not considered true scientific predictions.

Creating an experimental plan is a process that requires very meticulous thought. You need to be aware of all possible factors and account for their influence on the subject at hand. To be able to test hypotheses all variables must be under the control of the individual conducting the experiment. The variable that is manipulated is considered the independent variable, while the response variable is termed the dependent variable. The dependent variable is the measurable observed response seen in the experiment. For example, if the objective is to determine the effect of exercise on heart rate, then the measured value, heart rate, is the dependent variable because the value is dependent on the manipulation in the experiment, the exercise (independent variable).

For an ideal experiment to occur, only the independent variable can vary in the experiment during the course of multiple trials. Ensuring that this occurs is essential in standardizing the experimental plan. Part of this experimental process is the determination of an appropriate control group for the purposes of comparison. It is important to determine how the experimental plan will influence the subject being investigated under normal conditions before it can be determined that a relationship truly exists between the dependent and independent variables. Again, the experimental groups being investigated should only differ from the control group by a single factor, the independent variable. All experiments must be replicable. When it comes to replication of the experimental treatments try to repeat at least three times. When appropriate for the experiment it is typically best to reach at least a statistically significant sample size (n = 30). The data is then collected, put through statistical analysis and compared to the predictions.

Hypotheses at this point, once the statistical analysis has been reviewed and a summary of the data is available, can be evaluated for their validity. These conclusions are discussed along with the potential ramifications of these newly formed observations. It is always important to put your scientific work through peer-review with the ultimate aim of helping one another examine experimental design and interpret results. Once this occurs, these new observations can be reported. However, this is not the end. The process of scientific thought is cyclic. Once new results are obtained it should lead to the creation of new questions, which leads to a new experimental plan.

Procedure

As per the instructor's directions, read and discuss the scenario, below, that has been assigned to your class.

Scenario 1: Neuromuscular reaction time can be influenced by a number of different factors. Design an experiment where neuromuscular reaction time and the factors that influence it are tested among different individuals. This can be tested by measuring how quickly a person can grasp a falling meter stick.

Scenario 2: Termites are social insects that live in colonies, which can have millions of termites. Termites have a structured social system with the ability to communicate between individuals and groups using pheromone signals. Design and conduct an experiment where you test the termites' ability to communicate with each other.

Scenario 3: Blackworms, *Lumbriculus variegatus*, is a freshwater oligochaete worm (related to earthworms and leeches). Blackworms have a large dorsal blood vessel that is easy to observe under a microscope. Design and conduct an experiment that tests the effect of chemical exposure on the cardiovascular system of the blackworms.

Scenario 4: The house cricket, *Gryllus domesticus*, like many social animals have structure dominance hierarchies, which is based on the individuals' strength and influence over other crickets. Design and conduct an experiment where you test the benefits and costs to these individuals.

Making Observations

1. The first step in the scientific method is making observations. To begin exploring this scenario, as a group, summarize the group's collective knowledge about the scenario at hand. For example, what factors might influence the subject being tested? As the discussion proceeds, make notes below that summarize the group's knowledge and observations about the characteristics of the scenario and anything that could influence the scenario at hand.

Posing Questions

2. Scientific questions must be based on observations previously made. These newly developed questions are further refined and one of these questions is chosen to construct hypotheses. Use the observations gathered above and design scientifically answerable questions based on the assigned scenario. What criteria can be used to judge the quality of a "good question"? Propose questions based on these criteria and the gathered observations. These questions will then be presented and discussed as a class. Write the criteria points and proposed questions in the space below.

When defining a question to ask there are a lot of factors that must be considered including the funding needed to back the research. The scientific community looks to public and private institutions to help fund their research. To receive grant money there needs to be a proper justification for the questions being asked in the research project. For the proposed questions justify your reasoning for attempting to answer these question.

Developing Hypotheses and Predictions

3. A problem/question cannot be scientifically solved without reducing the problem into an appropriate hypothesis. The hypothesis should be identified before any research experiment is conducted. Remember this statement needs to be a clear statement of the intentions of the investigation and can be reasonably tested. Discuss the proposed questions, using the criteria of a "good question", and as a class, decide on the best question to formulate an appropriate scientific hypothesis. Write the question in the space provided below.

4. Formulate a scientific hypothesis based on the chosen question above. Discuss this hypothesis as a class. This must be a testable hypothesis through experimentation. Write the hypothesis below.

5. Develop an appropriate null hypothesis (H_o) and alternative hypothesis (H_a) based on the scientific hypothesis written above. These hypotheses must be testable through experimentation. Write the hypotheses below.

   Null Hypothesis (H_o):

   Alternative Hypothesis (H_a):

6. Translate your question-based hypothesis into a prediction. Write the prediction below. Make sure to also discuss the reasoning for your predictions.

Experimental Design

In the process of developing an experiment all the factors that could influence the results of an experiment must be considered before developing a protocol. To test the predictions and hypotheses, control and variables must be defined and taken into account. As the group discusses the potential factors that influence the experiment keep the overall design of the experiment in mind.

7. What are the factors involved in the experiment?

    - Which of the factors would be considered the independent variable(s)?

    - Which of the factors would be considered the dependent variable(s)?

    - What factors would need to be controlled during the experiment and how will they be controlled?

    - How will the experiment be standardized so that results can be comparable across all treatments to be able to collect and analyze data as a class? Why is setting standards for your experiment important?

8. Decide on the number of trials the experiment will include? Explain your reasoning.

9. Discuss your initial experimental plans with the class. Decide on an experiment plan which inquires about the developed hypotheses. Takes notes on the experiment plan in the space provided below.

Protocol Development

10. Write a step by step procedure that depicts how the experiment is to be conducted. The class will use this consensus protocol to conduct the experiment.

Organizing Data

11. Before performing any experiment, once the protocol has been identified there needs to be a plan in place to be able to clearly collect all the data necessary to be able to test the proposed hypotheses. Create a table in which the data will be recorded within the group. Also, create a data table that summarizes the class data. What statistical analyses should be included in the table, if any? Is qualitative or quantitative data being collected? Explain.

Group Data Table

Class Data Table

Once all aspects of the experiment have been explored and are clearly understood perform the experiment. Always record any observations you make during the experiment. Tabulate the collected data in the respective tables above. Write those non-quantitative observations below in an organized manner.

Experimental Observations:

Data Analysis

12. Translate the class data onto an Excel spreadsheet. This file will be shared electronically with the class for the purposes of creating appropriate graphs. When graphing the independent variable needs to be graphed against the dependent variable.

13. What trends do you see in the data and the differences observed between groups?

Making Conclusions

14. Return to the hypotheses (H_o and H_a) that were formulated at the beginning of the experiment. Compare them to the experimental results. Do you reject or fail to reject the hypothesis? Why? Cite the data used in making the decision. NOTE: When writing a scientific paper you NEVER simply write "I reject my null hypothesis because…" so avoid writing it here.

15. Provide an explanation as to why the results came out the way they did. Make sure to relate it back to the hypotheses and predictions.

16. As the experiment was conducted and the results were analyzed, additional questions probably came to mind. As a result of this inquiry and the results of this experiment, what would be some interesting questions to test if another experiment were to be conducted?

17. Evaluate the experiment design. Be critical of every aspect of the experiment. After having conducted the experiment is there anything else that should have be considered during the planning of the experiment. What errors could have occurred during the experiment? How can these errors be reduced in future experiment? Errors are inevitable in experiments. It can be defined as the difference between an observe measure of a quantity and its actual value. This is not always considered a mistake. Variability in data is part of analyzing collected data.

2

The Microscope & Cell Structure and Function

Objectives

1. Learn how to properly use both compound and dissecting microscopes.
2. Learn the basic parts of a microscope and their function.
3. Understand the relationship between magnification and resolution in microscopy.
4. Compare and contrast prokaryotes and eukaryotes
5. Review the basic principles, structures, and functions of cells and organelles

INTRODUCTION TO THE MICROSCOPE

The scientific field that studies microscopic samples, specimen that cannot be seen with the unaided eye, using a microscope is called Microscopy. It is not very well documented who exactly invented the microscope, but it is often attributed to two Dutch glass makers, Hans Lippershey (creator of the telescope) and Zacharias Janssen, in the late 1500s. In biology, many structures and organisms are too small to be detected and studied with the unaided eye. The human eye has a limited resolving power (200µm). To be able to overcome this problem an instrument needed to be invented to improve the human's eye resolution. This instrument was the microscope.

Resolution is the minimum distance between two points, where the two points are still distinguishable as separate points. For example, if two points are less than 200µm apart the human eye will perceive it as one object instead of two. Increased resolving power is possible because of the lens system that increases the magnifying power of the eye when observing a specimen through the microscope. Magnification is the process of increasing the apparent size of an object, but does not increase the size of the physical object. Keep in mind, resolution and magnification are two different concepts. Figure 2.1 demonstrates the difference between the terms on actual micrographs. Looking at 100x magnification the image to the left represents an image that was simply magnified to seem large, however, the image does not show distinct objects until the image has been resolved (the image to the right).

The modern optical or light microscope is based on the same optic principles as the original microscopes. There are three required elements to view an object through the microscope:

(1) An appropriate specimen

(2) An illumination source

(3) A lens system that focuses the illumination source on the specimen.

The Compound Light Microscope

The illuminating system, which concentrates light on the specimen, usually consists of a light source, condenser lens, and iris diaphragm. The light source is a light bulb located at the base of the microscope. The light source illuminates the specimen by passing light through a thin, almost transparent part of the specimen. The condenser lens, located immediately below the specimen, focuses light from the light source onto the specimen. Just below the condenser is the condenser iris

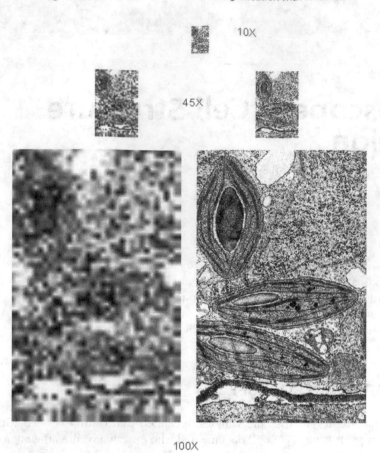

Figure 2.1
Magnification vs. Resolution.

diaphragm, a knurled ring or lever that can be opened and closed to regulate the amount of light reaching the specimen. When the condenser iris diaphragm is open, the image will be bright; when closed, the image will be dim.

The imaging system improves resolution and magnifies the image. It consists of the objective, ocular lenses and a body tube. The objectives are three or four lenses mounted on a revolving nosepiece (turret). Each objective is a series of several lenses that magnify the image, improve resolution, and correct irregularities in the image. The most common configuration for students microscopes includes four objectives: low magnification (4x), medium magnification (10x), high magnification (40x), and oil immersion (100x). Using the oil immersion objective requires special instructions. To avoid damaging your microscopes do not use the oil immersion objective during this exercise.

The ocular is the lens that you look through. Microscopes with one ocular are monocular microscopes, and those with two are binocular microscopes. Oculars usually magnify the image ten times. The body tube is a metal casing through which light passes to the oculars. In microscopes with bent body tubes and inclined oculars, the body tube contains mirrors and a prism that redirects light to the oculars. The stage secures the glass slide on which the specimen is mounted.

The microscope is a precision instrument and should always be handled with care. At all times you must observe the following rules for its transport, cleaning, use and storage:

1. When transporting the microscope, hold it in an upright position with one hand on its arm and the other supporting its base. Avoid jarring the instrument when setting it down. Never attempt to hold the microscope with just one hand.

2. Do not attempt to carry more than one microscope at a time.

3. Always gently place microscopes on the counter.

4. Minimize the use of eye make-up when using the microscopes. Make-up has the tendency to become deposited on the ocular lenses and it will result in an unclear image.

5. Use only special grit-free lens paper to clean the lenses. Clean all lenses before and after use.

2–2

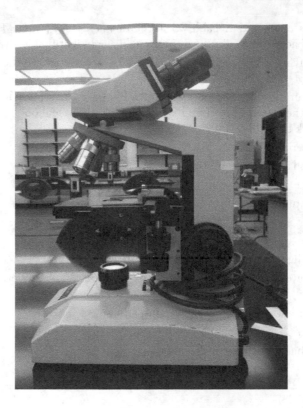

Figure 2.2

A compound light microscope.

6. Always begin the focusing process with the lowest power objective lens in viewing position, changing to the higher power lenses as necessary.

7. Never use the coarse adjustment knob with the high power or oil immersion lenses.

8. Always use a coverslip with temporary (wet mount) preparations.

9. Do not leave slides on the stage when the microscope is put away. Either put back the slides after their use or dispose of the slides properly as directed by the instructor.

10. Unplug the microscope light by grasping the plug, not the cord. Coil the cord around the microscope.

11. Make sure to never over rotate the course or fine adjustment knobs. If they are over rotated the knobs will get stuck and there is no way to fix it.

12. Before putting away the microscope make sure that:

   a. The light switch is in the off position.

   b. The scanning objective (4x), the low magnification objective, is in viewing position.

   c. Lower the position of the stage, using the coarse adjustment knob, as close to the base as possible.

   d. The cord should be wrapped around the microscope.

   e. There are no slides on the stage.

   f. The microscope is put back at its corresponding station number within the cabinet.

Task 1—USING THE MICROSCOPE

Procedure 2.1: Introduction to the Compound Light Microscope

1. Obtain two compound light microscopes per group from the cabinet. Record which microscopes are obtained. You will be responsible for the microscope. Using the sign-in sheet at the front of the room sign-out the microscopes obtained. These microscopes will be used by your group for the remainder of the semester.

   First Compound Light Microscope #: _____

   Second Compound Light Microscope #: _____

2–3

2. Using the parts of the microscope noted in Table 2.1, label the microscope parts in Figure 2.2. Make sure when labeling the figure you refer back to the microscope at the table and identify the corresponding part.

3. Using Table 2.1, after identifying where each part is on the microscope go down the list and identify the function of each part of the microscope.

4. Plug in the microscope and turn the illumination source on. Rotate the nosepiece to allow the low power (4X) objective lens to be in the viewing position. It should click into place. Looking through the oculars if it is completely black check the following
   - The objective clicked properly in place
   - The microscope is turned on and plugged in
   - There is light coming out of the lamp
   - The light intensity knob is turned on
   - The field iris is open
   - The condenser is in its proper place and open
   - Nothing is obstructing the light from coming up to the stage

   Always start at the lowest power objective available on a microscope when attempting to view a specimen using the microscope.

5. Locate the coarse adjustment knob. Turn it while watching the stage.

6. Locate the fine adjustment knob. Turn it while watching the stage.

7. Adjust the ocular lenses so that they fit the width between your eyes.

TABLE 2.1

PARTS OF THE MICROSCOPE

Part	Function
Nosepiece or Turret	
Objective	
Interpupillary Distance Indicator	
Stage Clip	
Stage	
Condenser Iris Diaphragm	
Illuminator Condenser	
Mechanical Stage Control Knob	
Substage Condenser Focusing Control Knob	
Substage Lamp	
Base	
Ocular(s)	
Body Tube	
Arm	
Slide Holder	
Coarse Focus Adjustment Knob	
Fine Focus Adjustment Knob	
Field Iris Diaphragm	

Questions

1. Why is it best to always start at the low power objective?

2. Which adjustment knob moved the stage more drastically?

3. Which adjustment knob should you use for the low magnification objective? Medium magnification objective? High magnification objective? Explain.

4. What general rules should be followed when focusing a microscope?

Diaphragm Control

The diaphragm (Figure 2.3) is an adjustable light barrier built into the condenser. It may be either an annular or an iris type. With an annular control, a plate under the stage is rotated, placing open circles of different diameters in the light path to regulate the amount of light that passes to the specimen. With the iris control, a lever projecting from one side of the condenser opens and closes the diaphragm. Use the smallest opening that does not interfere with the field of view. The condenser and diaphragm assembly may be adjusted vertically with a knob projecting to one side. Proper adjustment often yields a greatly improved view of the specimen.

5. Which type of diaphragm does your microscope have?

Figure 2.3
Diaphragm.

Procedure 2.2: Practice and Explore the use of microscopes

1. Obtain the letter "e" slide from the slide box and place it on the stage. As seen in Figure 2.4, make sure the microscope slide is held by the stage clip. Do not look through the oculars until instructed to do so during this procedure.
2. Move the stage back and forth (left and right, forward or backward) so that the "e" on the slide is directly beneath the objective lens. Pay close attention to the orientation and movement of the letter "e" with each change in position.
3. Look through the oculars to position the letter "e" on the slide in view. Use the coarse adjustment knob to move the slide to about 1 cm from the objective lens. Move the coarse adjustment knob until you can see the "e" through the lens.
4. Use the fine adjustment knob to get the letter "e" into sharp focus.
5. Move the letter "e" left and right. And then forward and backwards.
6. Using the nosepiece change the objective lens to the medium 10X power lens and repeat steps 4 and 5.
7. Using the nosepiece change the objective lens to the high 40X power lens and repeat steps 4 and 5. Do not use the course adjustment knob.

Questions

6. What is the difference between the orientation of the letter between the unaided eye and the microscope? What does that tell you about how the microscope processes the image?

7. How does the image move when the slide is moved to the left? Right?

8. How does the image move when the slide is moved up? Down?

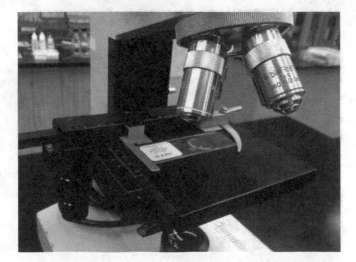

Figure 2.4

Slide properly place on the stage.

2–6

9.   What happens to the brightness of the view when you switch from the 4X to the 10X and again to the 40x objective lens?

10.   Why are mirrors important to the function of the microscope?

11.   Do mirrors influence the way slides are perceived to move under the microscope? Explain.

Task 2—MAGNIFICATION

1.   Examine the microscope and calculate the total magnification at each objective lens viewing position. Record this information in Table 2.2:

Equation 2.1: Total Magnification

$$Objective\ Magnification \times Ocular\ Magnification = Total\ Magnification$$

Questions

12.   How many times is the image of the "e" magnified when it is viewed through the highest power objective lens?

TABLE 2.2		
CALCULATION OF TOTAL MAGNIFICATION		
Objective magnification	Ocular magnification	Total magnification

13. If you did not know what you had on your slide (an "e") and you began examining it at the highest power, how could you determine it was an "e"?

14. How is the microscope properly put away?

Task 3—FIELD OF VIEW

The field of view (FOV) is the area that you can see through the ocular and objective (Figure 2.5). Knowing the size of the field of view is important because you can use it to determine the approximate size of an object you are examining. The field of view can be measured with a small clear plastic ruler.

Note: When calculating the FOV Area remember the shape of the field of view.

Procedure 2.3

1. Place a clear plastic ruler (mm) on the stage of the microscope.
2. Using the nosepiece place the lowest power objective lens in viewing position.
3. Using the course adjustment, try to get the ruler into focus. Only use the fine adjustment to sharpen the image. Measure the diameter of the field of view and record this in Table 2.3.

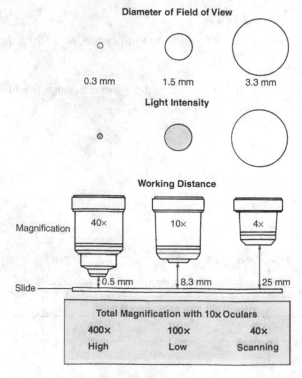

Figure 2.5

Field of View (FOV) Under Various Magnifications.

TABLE 2.3

FIELD OF VIEW CALCULATION

Objective	FOV diameter (mm)	FOV area (mm²)
4x		
10x		
40x		

4. FOV can easily be determined for the low power objective. At higher powers you will not be able to use the ruler to calculate FOV because the field of view is too small. Instead you can use the following formulas:

Equation 2.2: Field of View Medium Power Objective
$$FOVlow \times Maglow = FOVmedium \times Magmedium$$

or

Equation 2.3: Field of View High Power Objective
$$FOVmedium \times Magmedium = FOVhigh \times Maghigh$$

Use these formulas to calculate the FOV at medium 10X power objective and at high (40X) power objective. Record the results in Table 2.3.

5. Use the formula for the area of the circle to calculate the FOV for each magnification and record the results in Table 2.3.

Questions

15. Discuss the advantages and limitations of viewing specimens under highest magnification.

16. Discuss the advantages and limitations of viewing specimens under low-power objective?

17. Which magnification provides the largest FOV? Which provides the smallest? Explain.

18. Is there a change in the amount of light being emitted between the objective lenses? If so, rank them from brightest to dimmest and explain your reasoning.

19. Why is it more difficult to locate an object starting with the high power objective than with the low power objective?

20. How much more area can you see with the 4x objective than with the 40x objective?

Task 4—Depth of Field

Any microscopic specimen has depth as well as length and width; it is rare indeed to view a tissue slide with just one layer of cells. Organisms no matter how small are three dimensional, which is something that is not easy to see when initially viewing specimen under a microscope. Normally, when viewing a slide under the microscope two or three cell thicknesses can be observed. Therefore, it is important to learn how to determine relative depth with your microscope. When studying a live specimen under the microscope small enough organisms can travel across the depth of field, which can make it tricky when observing the specimen.

Procedure 2.4
1. Place the colored thread slide on the stage and secure it using the stage clip of the microscope.
2. Using the nosepiece place the lowest power objective lens in viewing position.
3. Use the coarse adjustment knob to get the colored threads into focus.
4. Sharpen the image with the fine adjustment knob.
5. Determine the number of threads on the slide
    Number of threads: _____
6. Determine the order in which the threads are placed on the slide.
7. Repeat steps 3 and 4 using the medium 10X power objective lens.
8. Repeat step 4 using the high 40X power objective lens.

Questions
21. How does depth of field affect viewing biological phenomena that are thick?

22. Are all three threads visible under the low power? Can they all be seen at the same time under higher power?

23. Using the microscope identify which color string is on top and which is on the bottom. Write your observations in the space below.

24. Which objective provides the greatest depth of field?

Task 5—WET MOUNT PREPARATION WITH BIOLOGICAL SPECIMENS

Procedure 2.5: Wet Mount Preparation

1. Place a drop of pond water (periphyton) on a clean slide.
2. Position the edge of a coverslip against the drop of pond water at a 45° angle
3. Gently lower the coverslip onto the slide.
4. Once prepared, view the slide with the microscope. Try to locate any microorganisms present on the wet mount and draw these observations in the space provided.
5. Take note of the tips below as you begin to look for organisms (Figure 2.6).

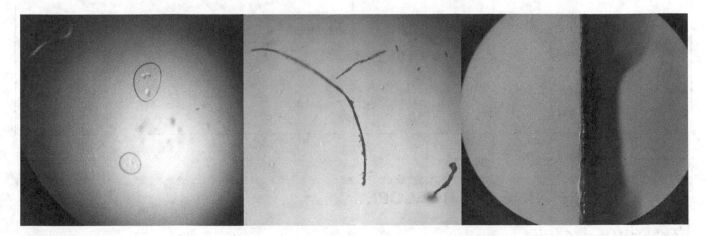

Figure 2.6
Microscope Tips. (a)These are not specimen, they are air bubbles; (b) these are not specimen, they are clothing fibers; (c) this is not a specimen, this is the edge of the cover slip.

Periphyton wet mount-Microorganisms

Magnification: _____

Procedure 2.6: Estimating the size of an object under the microscope

1. Use the diameter of the field of view for the power of magnification you are using.
2. Look through the ocular lens; estimate how many times the object will fit across the field of view. Pick two organisms in the FOV to perform this procedure.
3. Calculate the size of the object using the formula below

Equation 2.4: Object Size under the Microscope

$$\text{Size of object} = \frac{\text{diameter of field of view}}{\text{number of times object fits across field of view}}$$

Organism #1

Magnification: _____ Size: _____

Organism #2

Magnification: _____ Size: _____

Task 6—DISSECTING MICROSCOPE

Procedure 2.7

1. Obtain a dissecting light microscope from the cabinet. Record which microscope was obtained. You will be responsible for the microscope. Using the sign-in sheet at the front of the room sign-out the microscope obtained. This microscope will be used by your group for the remainder of the semester

   Dissecting Light Microscope #: _____

1. Familiarize yourself with all the parts of the microscope labeled in Figure 2.7.
2. Turn on the two light sources. On a dissecting microscope there is a light source from the stage and one from below.
3. Add a small amount of periphyton to a weigh boat or a petri dish and examine it under the dissecting microscope. Try to locate any macroorganisms present on the stage and draw these observations in the space provided.

Periphyton Macroorganisms

Magnification: _____

- Use a ruler to measure the FOV diameter at the lowest and the highest magnification.

    FOV diameter low power = _____
    FOV diameter high power = _____

- Now calculate the FOV area for both magnifications.

    FOV area low power = _____
    FOV area high power = _____

- Now calculate the size of an organism viewed under the microscope:

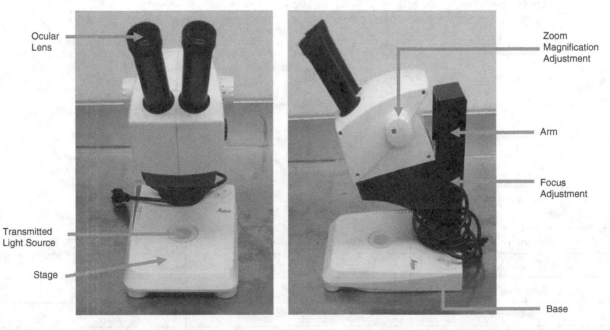

Figure 2.7

Major parts of a dissecting microscope.

25. Looking through the lens, move the Petri dish containing the "pond water" backwards and forwards, then left and right. Is the direction noted through the lens the same as when observed with the naked eye?

26. How does the image move when the object is moved to the left or right? Up and down?

Task 7—COMPARISON OF COMPOUND AND DISSECTING MICROSCOPES

Compare the two types of microscopes we examined today in Table 2.4. For this table use comparative terms (ie. Smaller vs. Larger).

Questions

27. Compare and contrast the structures found in the compound light microscope and the dissecting microscope.

28. What structures are found in the compound light microscope that are not in the dissecting microscope?

29. Discuss the advantages and disadvantages associated with each type of light microscope.

TABLE 2.4

Characteristic	Dissecting Light Microscope	Compound Light Microscope
Magnification		
Resolution		
Size of field of view		
Depth of field		

Cellular Structures & Functions

In 1665, Robert Hooke was the first to describe a cell as the basic unit of an organism. Upon his observation of thinly sliced pieces of cork (Figure 2.8), Hooke visualized small empty compartments that he termed *cellulae* (modern derivation = cell), which literally means "small room". Since Hooke's initial discovery, there have been several defining historical points that have characterized what a cell is and some of the most of important points are summarized in the cell theory.

The cell theory, proposed by Schleiden, Schwann and Virchow in the 1800s, states that (1) cells are the basic structural and functional unit of life, (2) all living organisms and their products are composed of cells, and (3) all cells come from pre-existing cells. Therefore, in order to understand even the simplest of biological processes, we need to understand cells, their structure and function.

Biologists recognize two cellular organizational plans: Prokaryotic and Eukaryotic cells (Table 2.5). Prokaryotic cells (Figure 2.9) lack a nuclear envelope and thus a nucleus and membranous cytoplasmic organelles. There are two major organismal groups that fall in the category of prokaryotic cells: Bacteria and Archaea. Eukaryotes have many structural features that prokaryotes lack. Only organisms that fall into the Domain Eukarya (protists, plants, fungi, and animals) are considered to have a eukaryotic organizational plan. Although these two types of cells are very different, they share many characteristics. A plasma membrane always surrounds a cell and regulates the movement of materials into and out of the cell. Both types of cells have similar types of enzymes found in the fluid-like filled area within the membrane termed the cytoplasm, depend on DNA as the hereditary material, and have ribosomes that function in protein synthesis.

Task 8—PROKARYOTIC CELLS

All members of the Kingdoms Arachaebacteria and Eubacteria have cells of the prokaryotic type. Although Archaeans and Bacteria look identical under the light microscope, they differ in their chemical composition and are completely unrelated to one another. Bacteria typically have a peptidoglycan structured cell wall and a cytoplasmic membrane, while Archaeans do not have peptidoglycan in their cell wall, but do have a membrane holding the cytoplasmic components of the cell together. Archaeans are often found in extreme environments, like hot springs, in which most Bacteria cannot survive. Archaens have stronger chemical bonds in the interactions that hold the membrane together and it is this that allows this cell to survive in extreme conditions.

A.　　　　　　　　　　　　　　　　B.

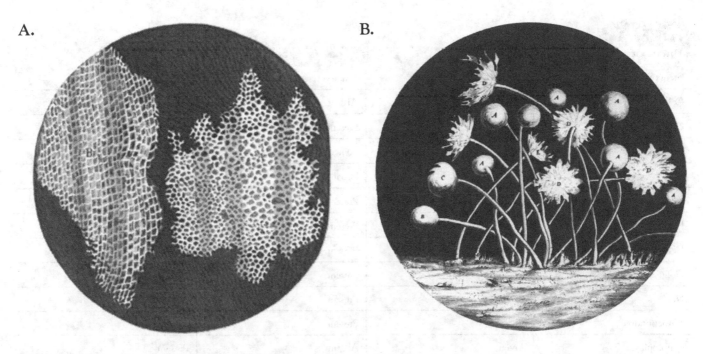

Figure 2.8

(a) Cell walls in cork tissue, as drawn by Hooke in 1665. (b) Hooke's *Micrographia*. Hooke's spore drawing in 1665.

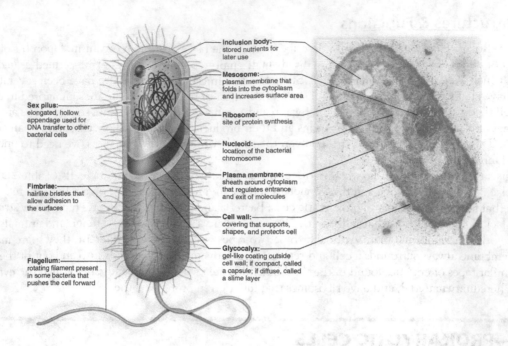

Inclusion body: stored nutrients for later use

Mesosome: plasma membrane that folds into the cytoplasm and increases surface area

Ribosome: site of protein synthesis

Nucleoid: location of the bacterial chromosome

Plasma membrane: sheath around cytoplasm that regulates entrance and exit of molecules

Cell wall: covering that supports, shapes, and protects cell

Glycocalyx: gel-like coating outside cell wall; if compact, called a capsule; if diffuse, called a slime layer

Sex pilus: elongated, hollow appendage used for DNA transfer to other bacterial cells

Fimbriae: hairlike bristles that allow adhesion to the surfaces

Flagellum: rotating filament present in some bacteria that pushes the cell forward

Figure 2.9
Prokaryotic cell

Cyanobacteria

The common name "blue-green algae" for cyanobacteria characterizes the primary feature of about half the organisms found in this classification. The defining characteristic and the common name are derived from the pigments phycocyanin (blue) and chlorophyll (green) present that give them their color. These pigments are not contained within membrane-bound chloroplasts, like in eukaryotic plant cells. However, despite not having chloroplasts cyanobacteria still photosynthesize and

TABLE 2.5

PROKARYOTES VS. EUKARYOTES

Structure	Prokaryote	Eukaryote (Animal)	Eukaryote (Plant)
Cell Wall	Present	Absent	Present
Cell Membrane	Present	Present	Present
Flagella	Sometimes	Sometimes	Absent (mostly)
ER	Absent	Usually Present	Usually Present
Ribosomes	Present	Present	Present
Microtubules	Absent	Present	Present
Centrioles	Absent	Present	Absent
Golgi Apparatus	Absent	Present	Present
Nucleus	Absent	Present	Present
Mitochondria	Absent	Present	Present
Chloroplasts	Absent	Absent	Present
Chromosomes	Single circle of DNA	Multiple	Multiple
Vacuoles	Absent	Small	Present and large

2–16

actually produce the majority of the earth's oxygen supply. All cyanobacteria are prokaryotes and most are surrounded by a gelatinous matrix, called a mucilaginous sheath. They live in soils, on moist surfaces, and in water (can be found easily in South Florida pond waters). Cyanobacteria are the largest of the prokaryotes and are easily seen using the compound light microscope.

Procedure 2.8

1. Examine a prepared slide of *Oscillatoria* and one of *Gloeocapsa*. Sketch each organism in the space provided below. Note the magnification at which you viewed your specimens.

2. On clean slides, prepare a wet mount of *Oscillatoria* and another of *Gloeocapsa*. Compare your observations to those previously visualized using prepared slides.

Observations of Cyanobacteria Wet Mounts

Oscillatoria Magnification: _____	*Gloeocapsa* Magnification: _____

Questions

30. Were you able to locate nuclei in either species? Did you expect to? Explain.

31. Is *Oscillatoria* a prokaryote or eukaryote? *Gloeocapsa*? Explain your reasoning.

32. Are there chloroplasts present in *Oscillatoria*? *Gloeocapsa*? Explain.

33. Where are the pigments located in the cyanobacteria that you examined? Are they present throughout the entire organism or only in certain locations?

34. How does the cell morphology differ between the two species of cyanobacteria?

35. How many cells are held together within one sheath of *Gloeocapsa*?

Task 9—EUKARYOTIC CELLS

Eukaryotes evolved approximately 1.5 billion years ago. In general, eukaryotic cells tend to be much larger and have a more complex structural design than prokaryotes since they possess a membrane-bound nucleus as well as a number of other membrane-bound organelles (Table 2.5).

The similarities observed between the prokaryotes and eukaryotes led to the development of the Endosymbiotic Theory. This theory proposes that eukaryotic cells arose from a prokaryotic ancestor (Figure 2.10). By engulfing and establishing a

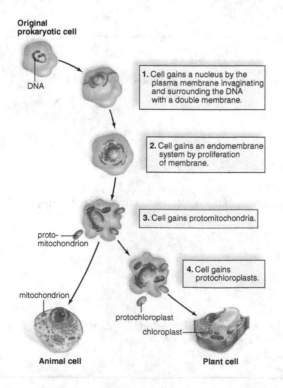

Figure 2.10

The endosymbiotic theory.

2–18

symbiotic relationship with cells that could undergo photosynthesis (photosynthetic bacteria) and create energy (ATP) through cellular respiration (aerobic bacteria), this new cell type has an advantage over its more ancestral form. The new relationship allowed the host ancestor cell to provide protection to the engulfed energy-producing cell and provide nutrients to the engulfed cells, while the engulfed cells allowed for metabolic processes like cellular respiration to occur within the host, a crucial evolutionary adaptation. The creation of this symbiotic relationship was the first step in moving towards a compartmentalized cell with each compartment (organelle) maintains an important and unique function.

Questions

36. Based on the endosymbiotic theory, some of the eukaryotic organelles have prokaryotic origins. Which organelles do you think these are and why?

37. What evidence would you need to gather to support the endosymbiotic theory? Explain how each piece of evidence would support the theory. (Hint: consider the structure of the modern eukaryotic cell)

Task 9A—EXPLORING PLANT CELLS

Plant and animal cells share most of the same organelles (Table 2.5). These include: (1) membrane-bound nucleus (contains genetic material, *i.e.* DNA, and is the control center of the cell), (2) cytoplasm, (3) endoplasmic reticulum (network of tubules used for protein translation and transport), (4) Golgi apparatus (processes proteins and lipids), (5) ribosomes (aid in translation of the genetic code) and (6) mitochondria (used for aerobic respiration). However, structures like chloroplasts (used for photosynthesis), the cell wall (surrounds the plasma membrane), and the central vacuole (contains water, ions, nutrients and waste products) are unique to plant cells (Figure 2.11).

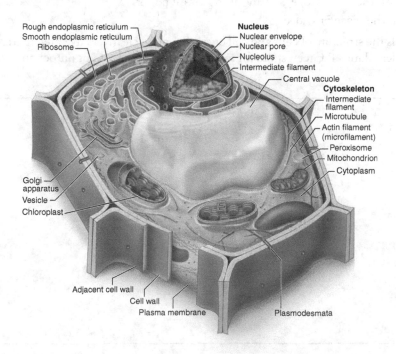

Figure 2.11
Plant cell structure.

Procedure 2.9: Examine Plant Cells

1. Collect one leaf from a sprig of *Elodea* and place the leaf, with the top surface facing up onto a clean slide.
2. Add one drop of pond water (same water sample that the *Elodea* came from).
3. Properly add a coverslip, as instructed during the preparation of a wet mount.
4. Examine this slide with the compound light microscope. Remember to always start on low power and then move to a higher magnification. Draw the specimen in the space provided.

Elodea

Magnification: _____

5. From an onion bulb collect one thin piece of epidermis by peeling the thinnest layer possible from each scale using forceps (Figure 2.12). The onion preparation should be about 1-cell thick.
6. Add 1 drop of 0.1% neutral red to the piece of onion.
7. Place a cover slip over the onion.
8. Set to stain for 5–10 minutes before visualizing.
9. Examine this slide with the microscope, starting at the lowest power.
10. Draw what you see in the space provided:

Staining often reveals the structure of cells and cell organelles more clearly. A dye preferentially stains some parts of the cell while leaving others clear. Janus B Green stain, for instance, preferentially stains mitochondria.

Onion-Neutral Red Stain

Magnification: _____

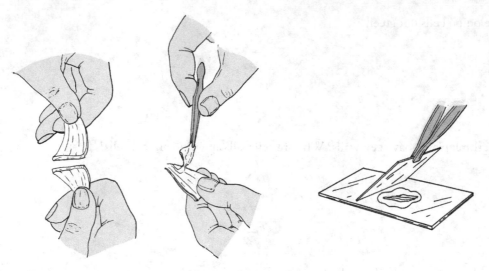

Figure 2.12

Preparing a wet mount of an onion epidermis.

Questions

38. What shape are the *Elodea* cells? What shape are the onion cells? Are they round or do they have distinct sides?

39. Try to determine how many cells thick your leaf and onion is by focusing up and down through the layers of cells.

40. What cell structures are visible? What are the functions of these structures? Make sure to label these structures in your scientific drawing above.

41. Are there any visible chloroplast? Explain your reasoning.

42. Why are the onion cells not green?

43. Why do you think plants have cell walls? Why are cell walls absent in animal cells?

44. Locate the chloroplasts within the cells. Try to estimate of the number present in one cell. Where in the cell do you generally find the chloroplasts?

45. Locate the central vacuole. Since it contains water, what should you see within it? Should there be any shapes or colors? This information should help you to locate it.

46. Locate the nucleus in the *Elodea* leaf. It may be pressed against the edge of the cell by the vacuole and may appear gray compared to the surrounding chloroplasts which are green. To enhance visibility, add a drop of iodine to the slide.

Task 9B—ANIMAL CELLS

Procedure 2.10: *Examine Animal Cell*

1. Using a toothpick, gently scrape the inside of your cheek.
2. Add one drop of water to a clean slide.
3. Stir the scrapings from the toothpick into the drop of water and then add a drop of methylene blue followed by a coverslip.
4. Sketch a few of the cells in the space provided. Label any visible organelles on your drawing.
5. Sketch a few of the cells in the space provided. Label any visible cellular structures on your scientific drawing.

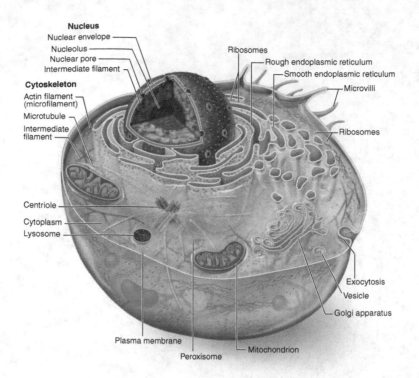

Figure 2.13
Animal cell.

Human Epithelial Cell- Methylene Blue Stain

Magnification: _____

Questions
47. What structure are visible in the cheek cells? Make sure to label the structures in the sketch above.

48. Compare and contrast the structural components of the cheek and onion cells.

3

Membranes

Objectives

- Investigate the nature of the cell membrane
- Explore how compounds or molecules pass through differentially permeable membranes
- Investigate Osmoregulation

CELL MEMBRANES

Cells cannot survive as independent entities from their environment. It does not matter whether the cell functions as a unicellular organism or as part of a system of tissues that make up an multicellular organism there needs to be a way to maintain a communication system with either the environment around the cells or other cells. Cells receive important nutrients and signal from the environment around them. At the same time, cells needs to have a system where they prevent unwanted or harmful chemicals from entering the cell's cytoplasm. Cells utilize the plasma membrane to regulate the communication between cells and the environment.

The fluid mosaic model is the widely accepted model for membrane structure. These membranes consist of a "fluid" portion which includes the phospholipid bilayer. A phospholipid molecule is composed of a phosphate group and two fatty acids bonded to a glycerol molecule (Figure 3.1). Phospholipids naturally position themselves into two layers, with the tails facing the interior of these two layers. These phospholipids self-assemble the way that they do because of the hydrophobic (water-fearing) and hydrophilic (water-loving) interactions between the layers. The phospholipid molecule itself has both hydrophobic and hydrophilic sections (head- hydrophilic; tail- hydrophobic). A molecule with this type of composition is termed an amphipathic molecule, a molecule with hydrophobic and hydrophilic sections (Figure 3.2). The "mosaic" portion of the model includes primarily the many types of proteins that are seen within the membrane. These proteins can either be found traversing the membrane, on the inside or outside directly attached to other membrane components, or some intermediate positioning. The majority of these molecules chemical nature is also amphipathic so that they can be placed within the membrane. These proteins have many functions including enzymatic, cell-to-cell identity markers, etc.

It is this chemical nature of the membrane that allows the membrane to be selectively permeable only allowing small, nonpolar and lipid-soluble molecules to pass through the phospholipid bilayer. Molecules that are too large, polar and/or hydrophilic can only enter the cell via transmembrane proteins. These proteins permit and facilitate the passage of specific molecules and polar ions across the membrane and also serve as receptors for communication between cells.

Questions

1. What determines the flow of water through the membrane?

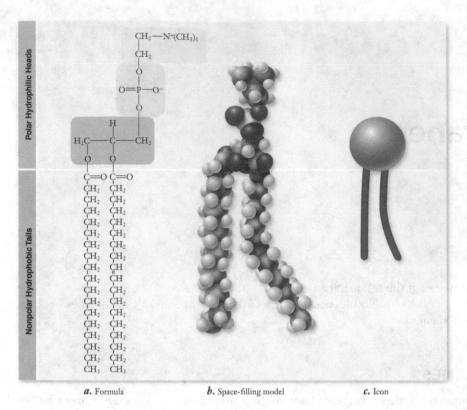

a. Formula   **b.** Space-filling model   **c.** Icon

Figure 3.1

Structure of a Phospholipid.

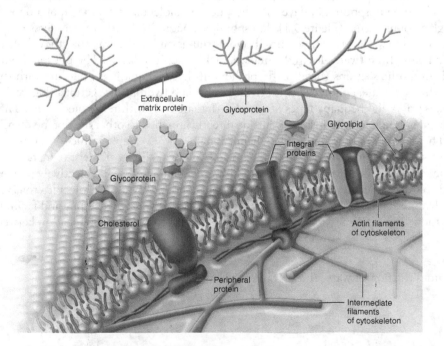

Figure 3.2

(a) Fluid Mosaic model of the Cell Membrane.

Task 1—DIFFUSION

Diffusion is the passive movement of a substance from an area of high concentration to an area of low concentration (Figure 3.3). The speed and direction at which movement, as a result of diffusion, occurs depends on the concentration gradient, heat, and pressure between the two areas, but can also be affected by the weight/size of the substance. Molecules travel from an area of higher solute concentration, heat and pressure to an area of lower solute concentration, heat and pressure, without the required use of energy. This would be a form of passive transport. To determine the rate of diffusion the steepness of the gradient and the size, polarity and solubility of the solute needs to be analyzed. When looking at biological systems, temperature and pressure is maintained relatively constant through homeostasis, a requirement for all living organisms. Thus, when analyzing diffusion it is typically best to look at relative concentrations to determine the rate at which molecules move through a particular area.

a.   b.   c.   d.

Figure 3.3
Diffusion.

Procedure 3.1: Diffusion of solute through liquid

1. Obtain two pieces of string and one piece of water-soaked dialysis tubing.
2. Seal one end of the bag as demonstrated by the instructor. The ends of the tube must be sealed tightly to prevent leaks.
3. Add 10 mL of starch suspension into the dialysis bag.
4. Seal the bag. It must be sealed tightly to prevent leaks.
5. Gently rinse the outside of the bag with water.

6. To a 250 mL beaker add 200 mL of tap water followed by approximately 3 mL of iodine. Place the bag containing the starch suspension into this beaker (Table 3).

7. Observe any color changes in the two areas of concentration (inside and outside the bag)

Based on what you know about diffusion, formulate scientific hypotheses and statistical (Ho and Ha) hypotheses for what you expect to occur in the bag over time. Write both hypotheses in the space provided and explain your reasoning for each.

Scientific:

H_o:

H_a:

(a) MAKE PREDICTIONS:

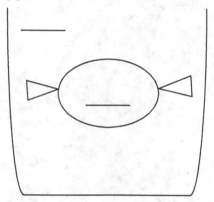

(b) INITIAL OBSERVATIONS:

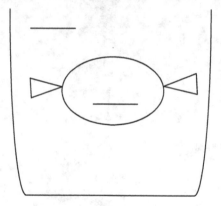

Figure 3.4
Diffusion through liquid Experiment (a) Predictions and (b) Initial Observations.

- Provide a written explanation of the predictions in the space below.

Questions

2. What is the best explanation for the color change that occurred?

3. Based on your results, which molecules passed through the membrane? Explain.

4.   Based on your results, which molecules did not pass through the membrane? Explain.

5.   Describe any problems you may have encountered during your experiment. Did this affect your results? If so, explain how.

6.   (a) Is your null hypothesis or alternative hypothesis supported by your data? Explain. (b) Do you reject or fail to reject your null hypothesis?

Task 2—BROWNIAN MOVEMENT

Brownian movement is the random movement of molecules in response to heat. This phenomenon can be observed by placing a India Ink dye under the microscope.

Procedure 3.2

1.   Place a small drop of the India Ink on a clean slide. Add a coverslip.

2.   Examine this slide with the microscope. Once in focus, look for movement (vibration) of the black dye molecules. Be patient, it may take the microscope light a few minutes to heat up your slide.

Based on what you know about diffusion, formulate scientific hypotheses and statistical (H_o and H_a) hypotheses for what you expect to occur on the slide over time. Write both hypotheses in the space provided and explain your reasoning for each.

Scientific:

H_o:

H_a:

Based on the hypotheses make note of your predictions below.

Describe your observations in the space below

Draw what initial observations were made when first view the India Ink slide under the microscope

```
┌─────────────────────────────────────────────────────────────────┐
│  Brownian Movement-Initial                                        │
│  Magnification: _____                                         │
│                                                                   │
│                                                                   │
│                                                                   │
│                                                                   │
│                                                                   │
│                                                                   │
└─────────────────────────────────────────────────────────────────┘
```

Draw the final observations made of the India Ink slide under the microscope

```
┌─────────────────────────────────────────────────────────────────┐
│  Brownian Movement-Final                                          │
│  Magnification: _____                                         │
│                                                                   │
│                                                                   │
│                                                                   │
│                                                                   │
│                                                                   │
│                                                                   │
└─────────────────────────────────────────────────────────────────┘
```

Questions

7.   What factors control the Brownian Motion?

8.   What direction are the particles moving?

9.   How does your last observation differ from your first? Explain.

10.   How does Brownian motion affect the rate of diffusion?

11.   Do you reject or fail to reject your null hypothesis? Explain.

Task 3—CELL SURFACE AREA TO VOLUME RATIO AND DIFFUSION

Most cells are microscopic. Very few, like the eggs we eat, are visible to the unaided eye. Why have cells evolved to be small versus very large structures visible to the human eye? How does this relate to cell surface area to volume ratio? The answer lies in how cells interact with their environment. Design an experiment that tests this question using the materials present in the lab. Keep in mind all of the steps of the Scientific Method. Write your full experiment plan in the space below.

Task 4—OSMOSIS

Osmosis (Figure 3.5) is the transport of water through a semi-permeable membrane down its concentration gradient. Osmosis is responsible for the fluid transport out of the kidney tubules and gastrointestinal tract, into capillaries, and across cell membranes. Tonicity classifications are relative terms describing the solute concentration of one environment to another. Hypertonic solutions contain a higher solute concentration than a compared area of solute concentration. When concentrations are the same between both solutions, the two areas are considered isotonic. Hypotonic refers to a solution that has a lower solute concentration than the solution on the opposing side of the membrane.

Organisms maintain homeostasis through osmoregulation, the active regulation of the osmotic pressure of their fluids. Osmotic pressure comes from the ability of a solvent and the inability of a solute to pass through a semi permeable membrane. When cells are placed in extreme environments, drastic effects on the cells can be observed. Sheep's red blood cells lyse when placed in a hypotonic solution, a process called hemolysis (Figure 3.7). When plant cells are placed in hypertonic solutions plasmolysis occurs (Figure 3.8). This process involves the loss of water through osmosis, which causes the plant's plasma membrane to pull away from the cell wall.

TABLE 3.1

OSMOSIS

Concentration	Hypotonic	Isotonic	Hypertonic
Solute inside	Lower	Same	Higher
Solute outside	Higher	Same	Lower

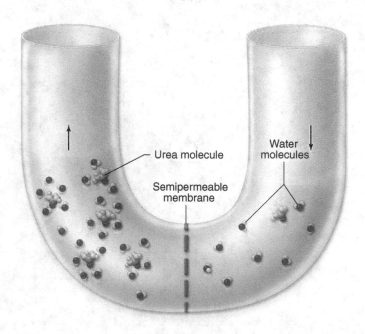

Figure 3.5
Osmosis.

Procedure 3.3

1. Fill the bowl at your station with tap water.

2. Fill the 250 mL beaker at your station with 25% sucrose.

3. Team up into pairs within your group. Each pair will be responsible for preparing two dialysis bags. Team one will prepare Bags A and B with 10 mL of tap water. Team two will prepare Bag C with 10 mL 10% sucrose and Bag D with 10 mL 25% sucrose. Make sure to include a label (written in pencil) into the correct bag.

4. Once the four bags are prepared, carefully dry them with a paper towel. Weigh each bag on the scale provided and record the weights in Table 5.

5. Simultaneously, place Bag A in 250 mL beaker containing 25% sucrose and bags B, C and D into the large bowl of tap water. Set your timer for 15 min.

6. After each 15 min interval (total time = 45 min) remove each bag, dry and weigh it. Record the weight for each bag in Table 5. After weighing, place the bags back into the correct beaker, and then calculate the change in weight from the previous measurement taken.

Based on what you know about osmosis, formulate scientific hypotheses and statistical (H_o and H_a) for what you expect to occur (in relation to bag weight) in each of the bags over time. Write both hypotheses in the space provided and explain your reasoning for each.

Scientific:

H_o:

H_a:

MAKE PREDICTIONS:

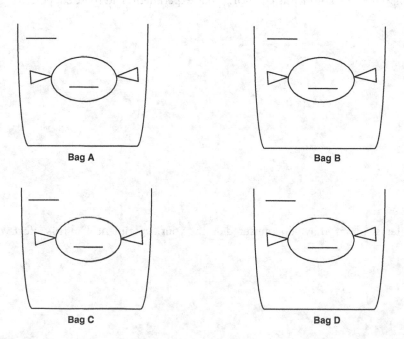

Figure 3.6

Using the figure 3.6a–d above, draw in the movement of water according to your predictions. Use the table below to explain the reasoning for your predictions.

TABLE 3.2

OSMOSIS EXPERIMENT PREDICTIONS

Bag	Explanation
A	
B	
C	
D	

TABLE 3.3

OBSERVED RESULTS

	0 min	15 min		30 min		45 min	
Bag A	Initial Wt.	Total Wt.	Wt. Change	Total Wt.	Wt. Change	Total Wt.	Wt. Change
Bag B							
Bag C							
Bag D							

- Using Excel, construct a graph that depicts the changes noted in each bag over time. Make sure to label the axes correctly and plot each bag as a separate curve.

Questions

12. Describe any changes observed or measured during your experiment. Did these support your predictions? Explain.

    Bag A:

    Bag B:

    Bag C:

    Bag D:

13. Describe any problems you may have encountered during your experiment. Did this affect your results? If so, explain how.

14. (a) Is your null hypothesis or alternative hypothesis supported by your data? Explain. (b) Do you reject or fail to reject your null hypothesis?

15. Which bag had the highest rate of osmosis? How can you tell? Why?

Task 5—HEMOLYSIS OF BLOOD CELLS

Blood cells provide an additional model to study osmosis and diffusion. If blood cells are placed in a hypotonic solution, water will rush in causing the cells to swell and eventually burst (hemolysis). On the other hand, if blood cells are placed in a hypertonic solution, water will rush out of the cells and they will crenate or shrivel (Figure 3.7).

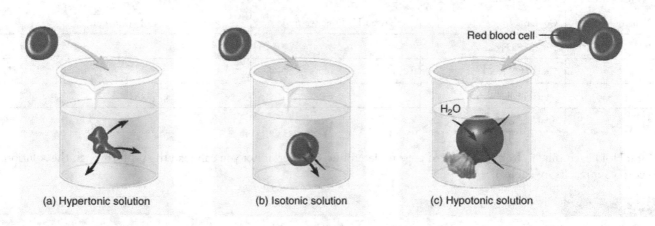

(a) Hypertonic solution   (b) Isotonic solution   (c) Hypotonic solution

Figure 3.7
Osmosis in Red Blood Cells.

Procedure 3.4

1. Obtain four test tubes and add 5 drops of sheep blood from the refrigerator and label them 1–4.

2. To tube 1 add 5 mL of 10% NaCl, to tube 2, 5 mL 0.9% NaCl, to tube 3, 5 mL of distilled water and to tube 4 add 5 mL of sucrose solution.

3. Cover each tube with parafilm before inverting to mix the solutions.

4.   Formulate hypotheses (Scientific, H$_o$ and H$_a$) regarding your expectations for the outcome to the blood cells in each tube. State your hypotheses in the space provided. Make sure to include your reasoning.

Scientific:

H$_o$:

H$_a$:

5.   Hold each tube in front of a printed page to determine whether or not you can read the print through the solution. Record your results in Table 6.

TABLE 3.4

RBC PREDICTIONS TABLE

Tube #	Contents	Readable Print (yes/no)	Explanation
1	5 mL 10% NaCl		
2	5 mL 0.9% NaCl		
3	5 mL distilled water		
4	5 mL sucrose solution		

Note: Hold each tube in front of a printed page to determine whether or not you can read the print through the solution. Record your results in Table 3.5.

TABLE 3.5

RBC RESULTS TABLE

Tube #	Contents	Readable Print (yes/no)	Explanation
1	5 mL 10% NaCl		
2	5 mL 0.9% NaCl		
3	5 mL distilled water		
4	5 mL sucrose solution		

Questions

16.   Did the results correspond to your predictions?

17.   Describe any problems you may have encountered during your experiment. Did this affect your results? If so, explain how.

18. (a) Is your null hypothesis or alternative hypothesis supported by your data? Explain. (b) Do you reject or fail to reject your null hypothesis?

19. If a person's blood volume drops due to injury or sever dehydration, why do doctors administer isotonic saline intravenously instead of pure water?

20. What osmotic regulatory challenges would a fish living in freshwater have versus a fish living in salt water?

Task 6—OSMOREGULATION

<u>Directions:</u> In the table below, predict the reaction of the following cell types in the different environments.

TABLE 3.6

OSMOREGULATION PREDICTIONS			
	Extracellular Environment		
	Hypotonic _____ % NaCl	Isotonic _____ % NaCl	Hypertonic _____ % NaCl
Sheep's Blood (RBC)			
Plant (Elodea)			

Procedure 3.5

I. Sheep's Blood- Red Blood Cells

1. Place a drop of the blood from tube 1 (from Task 5) onto a clean slide and then add a cover slip. Repeat the same procedure for tubes 2 and 3. Mark the slides with the appropriate tube number so that you can be certain which slide contains blood from which tube.

2. Examine each slide under the microscope. Determine if the cells are crenate (shriveled), have burst (so only fragments remain) or whether they appear healthy and round. Record the results in Table 3.7.

Procedure 3.6

II. Elodea Cells

1. Collect one leaf from a spring of Elodea. Add a drop of isotonic solution to a clean slide. Place the leaf, with the top surface facing up, in the drop of isotonic solution on the slide. Add a coverslip.

2. Examine each slide under the microscope. Record your results in Table 3.7.

TABLE 3.7

OBSERVED RESULTS

	Extracellular Environment		
	Hypotonic _____ % NaCl	Isotonic _____ % NaCl	Hypertonic _____ % NaCl
Sheep's Blood			
Plant (Elodea)			

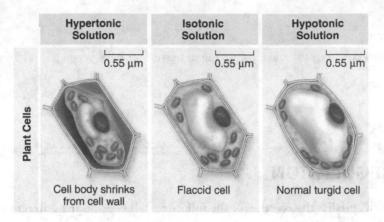

Figure 3.8

Response of plant cells to a. hypotonic and b. hypertonic extracellular environments.

Questions

21. Compare and contrast the reaction the animal cell had to the hypotonic solution compared to the plant cell.

22. Compare and contrast the reaction the animal cell had to the hypertonic solution compared to the plant cell.

23. What factors might affect the speed of water movement in or out of a cell?

24. Did the results correspond to your predictions?

25. Describe any problems you may have encountered during your experiment. Did this affect your results? If so, explain how.

26. (a) Is your null hypothesis or alternative hypothesis supported by your data? Explain. (b) Do you reject or fail to reject your null hypothesis?

Response of Single Celled Organisms to Environmental Stimuli

Living organisms respond to outside stimuli. Their ability to sense and respond to the local environment increases their survival rate. In this exercise, you will design an experiment to examine the response of an Amoeba to a particular environmental stimulus.

27. Choose the stimulus that you would like to test (e.g. temperature, light, salinity, acidity) and record it below.

28. Formulate hypotheses (H_o and H_a) about your predictions on how you expect the *Amoeba* to react in response to the stimulus. Write your hypotheses in the space provided.

29. Decide how to test your hypotheses. Describe your experimental design in the space below:

Enzymes

4

Objectives

- Learn about the function of enzymes.
- Understand and be able to predict how temperature affects enzyme activity.
- Understand how to collect and examine qualitative data.

INTRODUCTION

All biological processes, including growth, reproduction and metabolism, require a constant supply of energy. The production of this energy is accomplished through the thousands of chemical reactions that occur in cells and is regulated by biological catalysts called **enzymes**. Our everyday lives are dependent on these proteins and in some instances the absence of a particular enzyme can cause serious illness and in severe cases, even death. For example, tyrosinase deficiency, an enzyme needed for production of cellular pigments, causes albinism, while insufficient production of phenylalanine hydroxilase results in phenylketonuria (PKU), which can lead to severe mental retardation if left untreated.

The use of enzymes in our daily lives has significantly improved our standard of living. For instance, proteases and amylases, which are produced by the body to break down protein and starch, respectively, are also used commercially to bake bread, biscuits and crackers. Enzymes are also utilized in brewing processes for the production of alcohol, cheese, and detergents, as well as to tan leather products. In medicine, enzymes are important agents in the treatment of heart attacks (streptokinase dissolves blood clots in arteries of heart walls) and cancer (asparaginase is used for acute lymphocytic leukemia in children). Without enzymes, life would not be possible. Food would not be converted to energy and our bodies would not be able to replace old, damaged tissues with new, healthy ones. Cellular waste products would not be disposed of and ultimately, all cellular activity (metabolism, reproduction, growth) would cease.

Enzymes increase the rate of reactions by lowering the **activation energy**, the amount of energy required for chemical reactions to occur (Figure 4.1). Without these biocatalysts, all metabolic processes would take far too long to sustain life.

Most enzymes are proteins with three-dimensional shapes determined by their amino acid sequences. When a **substrate (reactant)** molecule binds to the highly specific **active site** of an enzyme, an **enzyme-substrate (ES) complex** is formed (Figure 4.2). The ES complex modifies the substrate's chemical bonds and initiates a series of chemical reactions resulting in the formation of a **product**. It is important to note that the enzyme itself is not changed or consumed in the reaction thus, it is reusable. As products are generated they are released from the enzyme's active site allowing other substrate molecules to bind.

The active site determines the specificity of every enzyme. Specificity can result from the charge, shape, and hydrophobic/hydrophilic characteristics of the enzyme and substrate molecules. Only reactants that match the geometric shape of the active site can bind to the enzyme. This specificity is also known as the "**lock and key model**" where the substrate (the key) fits into the active site (the lock) of an enzyme. However, as mentioned previously, the interaction between a substrate and the enzyme's active site is not static, it is dynamic. When a substrate binds to the enzyme, the active site is reshaped by the interactions of the enzyme's amino acid side chains with the substrate molecule. This protein remodeling enhances the overall binding of the reactant to the active site, increasing catalytic action. The ability of enzymes to mold their shape to enhance the fit of substrate molecules is known as the "**induced fit model**."

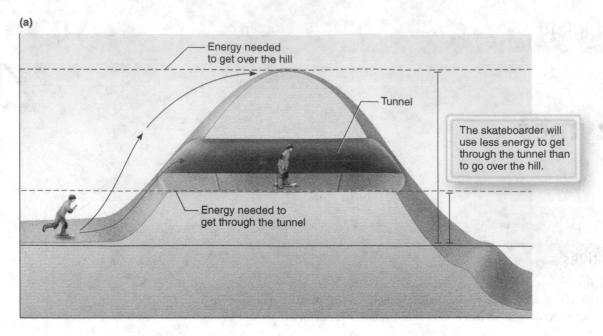

(a)

Energy needed to get over the hill

Tunnel

The skateboarder will use less energy to get through the tunnel than to go over the hill.

Energy needed to get through the tunnel

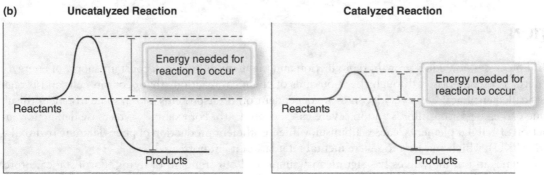

(b)

Uncatalyzed Reaction

Energy needed for reaction to occur

Reactants

Products

Catalyzed Reaction

Energy needed for reaction to occur

Reactants

Products

Figure 4.1

Enzymes lower the activation energy needed for chemical reactions.

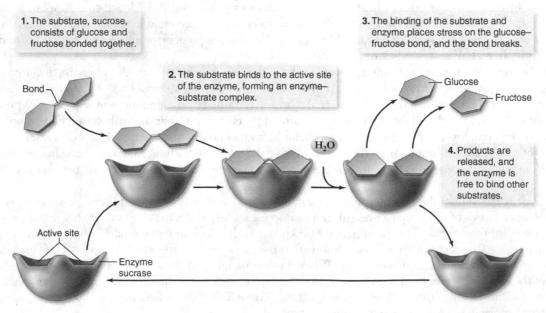

1. The substrate, sucrose, consists of glucose and fructose bonded together.

3. The binding of the substrate and enzyme places stress on the glucose–fructose bond, and the bond breaks.

2. The substrate binds to the active site of the enzyme, forming an enzyme–substrate complex.

Bond

Glucose

Fructose

H_2O

4. Products are released, and the enzyme is free to bind other substrates.

Active site

Enzyme sucrase

Figure 4.2

Substrate binding at the active site of an enzyme.

4–2

There are thousands of different enzyme types, each with a specific set of conditions at which it works best, its **optimal conditions**. An enzyme's optimal conditions often reflect the environment in which the organism is found. For instance, the optimum temperature for enzymes present in *Thermophilus aquaticus*, an extremophilic bacterium that inhabits hot springs, is about 70 °C. In contrast, peroxidase, an enzyme present at high concentrations in turnips, horseradish roots and potatoes, works best at temperatures around 45 °C.

Enzymatic activity is affected by multiple factors, including pH, substrate concentration, salt concentration, as well as the presence of inhibitors, activators and cofactors. Temperature affects the rate at which substrate and enzyme molecules collide. At temperatures greater than the optimal, the active site **denatures** (*i.e.* changes shape), decreasing or preventing substrate binding. Consequently, product formation is either reduced or completely arrested. At the other end of the spectrum, low temperatures decrease the movement of molecules, resulting in less contact between enzymes and substrates, which slows down the frequency and rate of reaction, and ultimately diminishes product formation. Although the effect of temperatures outside of the optimal range on substrate catalysis is the same, the mechanism through which enzyme activity is reduced, differs.

The objective of the current lab is two-fold; (1) to examine how variations in temperature affect the activity of the enzyme **amylase** and (2) to determine the optimal temperature for amylase from two different sources.

Amylase catabolizes starch polymers (a storage polysaccharide) into smaller subunits (monomers = saccharides) including maltriose, maltose and short oligosaccharides comprised of 2-20 monosaccharide units (Figure 4.3). Most organisms use these saccharides as a food source and to store energy (Figure 4.4). Both starch and amylase are important commercially in the production of syrups and other food products, as well as for fermentation and brewing processes.

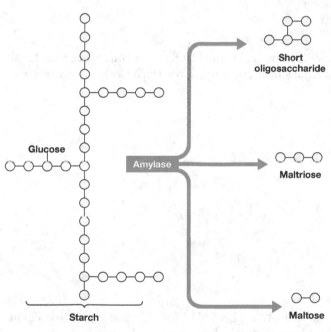

Figure 4.3
Starch digestion by amylase.

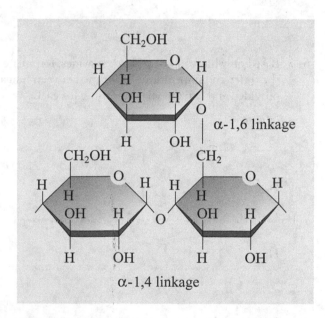

Figure 4.4
Starch molecule. Starch formed by the interlinking of multiple glucose units connected by alpha-1,4 and alpha-1,6 linkages.

Task 1—EFFECT OF TEMPERATURE ON AMYLASE ACTIVITY

The objective of this exercise is to determine the optimal temperatures for fungal, *Aspergillus oryzae*, and bacterial amylases. In addition, you will examine the effect of temperature on the ability of amylase to break down starch to maltose. You will monitor starch catalysis visually using the Iodine test, which turns from yellow to blue-black in the presence of starch.

Questions
1. Briefly in your own words describe how enzymes function.

2. What factors could affect the proper function of an enzyme?

3. Differentiate between dehydration synthesis and hydrolysis reactions.

4. Differentiate between catabolism and anabolism.

5. What criteria will you use to determine that starch has been catabolized?

6. Based on what you know about enzymes, formulate hypotheses (Scientific, H_o and H_a) for what you expect to occur at the different temperatures over time between fungal and bacterial amylase activity. Write the hypotheses in the space provided and explain your reasoning for each.

   Scientific:

   H_o:

   H_a:

7. Based on what you know about enzymes, formulate hypotheses (Scientific, H_o and H_a) for what you expect to occur at the different temperatures over time using bacterial amylase activity. Write the hypotheses in the space provided and explain your reasoning for each.

   Scientific:

   H_o:

   H_a:

8. Based on what you know about enzymes, formulate hypotheses (Scientific, H_o and H_a) for what you expect to occur at the different temperatures over time using fungal amylase activity. Write the hypotheses in the space provided and explain your reasoning for each.

Scientific:

H_o:

H_a:

TABLE 4.1

FUNGAL AMYLASE PREDICTIONS

Temperature (°C)	Expected Results	Reasoning
0		
40		
60		
95		

TABLE 4.2

BACTERIAL AMYLASE PREDICTIONS

Temperature (°C)	Expected Results	Reasoning
0		
40		
60		
95		

Important Notes

To determine the optimal temperatures for both enzymes, you will need to generate a class data set by combining your group's results with the data collected by the other groups in your class. These data sets are a required element in your lab reports.

Procedure

I. Experimental Setup

1. Place a napkin/paper under the spot plates (Figure 4.5) and across the top write Temperature (0°, 40°, 60°, 95° Celsius) and on the side write Time (0, 2, 4, 6, 8, 10 min).

2. Obtain 4 test tubes and label each with a different temperature (0°, 40°, 60°, 95° Celsius), enzyme source (B – Bacterial and F – Fungal) and your group number.

3. Obtain another 4 test tubes and label these with a different temperature, enzyme source (B or F), your group number and the letter S (for starch solution).

4. Add 5 mL of 1.5% starch solution into each of the test tubes labeled S.

II. Effect of Temperature on Amylase Activity

5. Add 1 mL of amylase into each of the test tubes that do not contain starch. If first assigned to do bacterial amylase place the amylase solution into the bacterial amylase designated test tubes. If assigned the fungal amylase place the amylase solution into the bacterial amylase designated test tubes.

6. Place all 4 test tubes containing starch and the 4 test tubes containing amylase into their respective temperatures.
   a. 0 °C into the ice bath,
   b. 40 °C into the 40 °C water bath,
   c. 60 °C into the 60 °C water bath,
   d. 95 °C into the 95 °C water bath.

7. Allow all tubes to equilibrate for 5 minutes in their respective temperatures.

8. Add 2–3 drops of iodine to each well at the 0 minutes row.

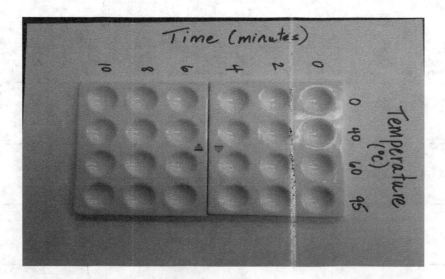

Figure 4.5

Spot plate setup.

4–6

9. At the end of the equilibration process, <u>without</u> **removing the tubes from their water baths**, transfer a few drops of the starch solution from each temperature treatment to the first row of the spot plate corresponding to time 0 minutes. **Make sure to use a separate transfer pipette for each temperature treatment.** Label each of your transfer pipettes with the correct temperature so that they can be reused for each time interval.

10. Within each temperature treatment, pour the starch solution into the tube containing amylase. Set your timer for 2 min at the moment of amylase addition.

11. Add 2–3 drops of iodine to each well at the 2 minutes row. This will be repeated before the transfer of each starch-amylase mixture to the spot plates.

12. After 2 min, use the correct transfer pipette for each temperature to remove a few drops of the starch-amylase mixture from each tube. Place 2–3 drops of the mixture in the second row (time = 2 min) on your spot plate under the corresponding temperature. Note the color changes and record your observations in Table 4.3 (bacterial amylase) or 4.4 (fungal amylase), depending on your amylase source. Note: You will be analyzing the CLASS DATA SET in your lab reports.

TABLE 4.3
BACTERIAL AMYLASE

		Temp (°C)							
		0		40		60		95	
		Color	#	Color	#	Color	#	Color	#
Time (min)	0								
	2								
	4								
	6								
	8								
	10								

TABLE 4.4
FUNGAL AMYLASE

		Temp (°C)							
		0		40		60		95	
		Color	#	Color	#	Color	#	Color	#
Time (min)	0								
	2								
	4								
	6								
	8								
	10								

13. After each additional 2 min, repeat step 11 and 12. Make sure that you add the starch-amylase mix to the correct wells for time and temperature.

14. At the end of the 10 min, note the temperature and the time at which 100% hydrolysis occurred (Figure 4.6).

15. Repeat the procedure using the other amylase type.

16. Use the color-coding scheme below to convert your results (qualitative data) into quantitative (numerical) data. In the column next to your color data, record the corresponding number.

Questions

9. Which of the variables is (are) the independent variable(s)?

10. Which of the variables is (are) the dependent variable(s)?

11. What variables serve as controls and what do they control for?

12. Based on the color findings, is starch present at time zero? Should starch be present? Why or why not?

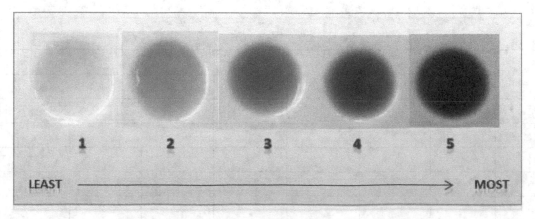

Figure 4.6
Starch hydrolysis.

13. Did your observed results reflect your predictions for fungal amylase activity (Table 1)? Explain.

    0

    40

    60

    95

14. Did your observed results reflect your predictions for bacterial amylase activity (Table 2)? Explain.

    0

    40

    60

    95

15. What do your results indicate about the optimal temperature for each type of amylase?

16. Explain the relationship between the amount of starch and maltose present during starch hydrolysis.

17. Do you reject or fail to reject your null hypothesis? Explain.

18. Explain the reasoning behind the changes seen at each temperature for fungal amylase.

    0

    40

    60

    95

19. Indicate which temperature had the fastest rate of reaction for fungal amylase activity. Explain.

20. Explain the reasoning behind the changes seen at each temperature for bacterial amylase.

    0

    40

    60

    95

21. Indicate which temperature had the fastest rate of reaction for bacterial amylase activity. Explain.

22. How does temperature affect the structure of the enzyme. Does this relate to enzyme activity?

23. Compare and contrast the rate of reaction for bacterial and fungal amylase activity.

24. Identify any possible sources of error which may have affected the results of this experiment.

25. How do the optimal temperature results for fungal amylase activity relate to environmental conditions for the organism's natural habitat?

26. How do the optimal temperature results bacterial amylase activity relate to environmental conditions for the organism's natural habitat?

27. If this same experiment were performed using human amylase how would the optimal temperature results for human amylase activity relate to normal human body temperature?

28. In the space below sketch graphs that would be representative of fungal amylase enzyme activity vs. change in temperature.

29. In the space below sketch graphs that would be representative of bacterial amylase enzyme activity vs. change in temperature.

30. If this experiment were performed using human amylase In the space below sketch graphs that would be representative of human amylase enzyme activity vs. change in temperature.

31. Why is it necessary to let the test tubes stand for 5 minutes in their various temperatures?

32. What was the purpose of the 0 minutes wells at each temperature?

Data Analysis

Because there is usually some degree of error introduced when we take measurements, scientists take multiple readings and then use statistics to get a more accurate representation of the true measurement and to be able to evaluate how accurate the sampling may have been. How much variation exists between each measure taken can give you an idea about accuracy. In general, scientists use two types of statistical calculations to measure variability: (1) **variance** and (2) **standard deviation**.

Variance is a measure of the dispersion of a set of data points around their mean value. Variance is a mathematical expectation of the average squared standard deviations from the mean.

$$Variance = \sum \frac{(x - x_{ave})}{(N - 1)}$$

The Standard Deviation is a measure of how spread out the numbers in the data set are. Its symbol is σ (the greek letter sigma). The formula is easy: it is the square root of the Variance. **Make sure to read the Simple Statistics link on the website for additional help.**

33. Using the values in the Table 4.5, perform all calculations necessary to obtain the variance and standard deviation for the data set.

TABLE 4.5

Measure Collected	Measure-Mean	(Measure-Mean)^2
12		
17		
32		
26		
22		
19		
13		
23		
20		
Sum (Σ) =		Σ =
Sample Size (N) =		N − 1 =
Mean =		Variance =
		Standard Deviation =

III. Generation of a class dataset (must be included in the lab report)

1. Combine the numerical data from each group. If there are 6 groups in your class, then each group should have a dataset for fungal amylase and another for bacterial amylase. Therefore, as a class, you should have 6 datasets for each amylase type.

2. Record your results in the log files (one for bacterial and one for fungal amylase). Make sure to include the results of every group in each cell of the table.

3. Based on the results of all groups, record the optimal temperature for amylase activity as well as the time for 100% hydrolysis to occur at the optimal temperature in the last two rows of each log file.

IV. For homework

1. Calculate the mean and standard deviation (SD) for each temperature and time for both enzymes. Record these values in the log files.

2. Using the numerical data collected in Tables 4.3 and 4.4, create a graph(s) in Excel that addresses the following questions:

    a. How does temperature affect amylase activity?

        i. You may choose to plot either starch or maltose concentration but make sure that you understand the relationship between the two compounds..

    b. Is starch catabolism equally efficient across all temperatures?

    c. Do fungal and bacterial amylases breakdown starch at the same temperature(s) and rate (time to completely hydrolyze starch)?

    d. What is the relationship between starch and maltose concentrations during starch hydrolysis?

3. Suggestions for graphing data:

    a. There is more than one way to present your data graphically. Each graph generated may show different aspects of your data and may explain the relationships between your variables in different ways. The key to figuring out the best way to show a particular relationship is by plotting the data and trying to interpret what the graph illustrates (you may need to plot the data using multiple approaches).

    b. You do not need a separate graph to answer each of the questions above but you may need to generate more than one graph to address the questions properly.

    c. When plotting your data, label the axes with a few words describing what is being measured and include units in parentheses [e.g. Time (min)]. Also remember to include a title for your graph.

    d. If you are plotting more than one variable on a graph, use different colors, symbols, or line patterns to differentiate between variables and create a legend to explain what each color/symbol represents.

4. Questions to consider when examining your data

    a. Is there a lot of variation between the group data for each time, temperature and amylase type?

        i. What can account for this variation? (**Hint:** consider methodology and experimental errors)

    b. Is there more variance for certain temperature treatments than for others? If so, what factors can explain the variance observed?

    c. What does your data suggest about the optimal temperatures for amylase from the two different sources?

        i. What about the time for hydrolysis?

Cellular Respiration

5

Objectives

- Understand the major events of glucose catabolism (cellular respiration): glycolysis, the citric acid cycle and oxidative phosphorylation.
- Compare and contrast the processes involved in aerobic and anaerobic respiration.
- Demonstrate carbon dioxide production during anaerobic respiration.
- Determine oxygen consumption during aerobic respiration.
- Measure the relative production of carbon dioxide by plants and animals.

INTRODUCTION

All living organisms have evolved a series of biochemical reactions, where organic molecules (carbon-based compounds; *e.g.* glucose) are enzymatically broken down. These universal series of reactions are termed Cellular Respiration. In this process, energy, in the form of adenosine triphosphate (ATP), is released and utilized by the cell for basic biological functions including growth, metabolism and cellular maintenance. The energy that ATP provides is stored in the bonds between the highly negatively charged phosphate groups (Figure 5.1a). This energy is available for cells to use once ATP is hydrolyzed (Figure 5.1b). Hydrolysis is the process of adding water to a macromolecule, like ATP a nucleic acid derivative, to break apart the chemical bonds that link the monomers of macromolecules together. Dehydration Synthesis is the process of removing water from a macromolecule to link monomers together by creating new chemical bonds to produce a macromolecule.

Oxidation-reduction or Redox reactions (Figure 5.2) are those in which electrons are transferred from one molecule to another and are known to play a pivotal role in cellular respiration. Reduction involves the gain of electrons or hydrogen atoms, while Oxidation involves the loss of electrons or hydrogen atoms. Two of the most important coenzymes, and are also nucleic-acid derivatives, involved in the process are **nicotinamide adenine dinucleotide (NAD$^+$)** and **flavin adenine dinucleotide (FAD$^+$)**. These molecules are reduced to NADH and FADH$_2$ when they acquire electrons, which are then transfer to other molecules involved in the process in order to generate the ATP required to maintain the metabolic processes of the cell.

There are two methods that the cell uses to synthesize ATP: (1) substrate-level phosphorylation and (2) oxidative phosphorylation. Substrate-level phosphorylation depends on the interaction between an enzyme (a kinase), its phosphorylated substrate, and the coenzyme adenosine diphosphate (ADP). Once bound to the active site of the enzyme, the high-energy substrate will donate its phosphate group to the lower energy ADP, which is also bound to the enzyme, to form ATP (Figure 5.3). Oxidative phosphorylation, however, is powered by basic proton motor force and occurs through the use of ATP Synthase.

Glycolysis produces 4 ATP molecules. These 4 ATP molecules are all formed through the use of a substrate-enzyme complex. The step seen in Figure 5.3 is actually the final step in Glycolysis, which is an example of substrate-level phosphorylation. Phosphoenolpyruvate (phosphorylated substrate) binds to the active site on pyruvate kinase (enzyme) and the phosphate group is transferred to ADP to make ATP. As a result, a very important intermediate product was made, pyruvate.

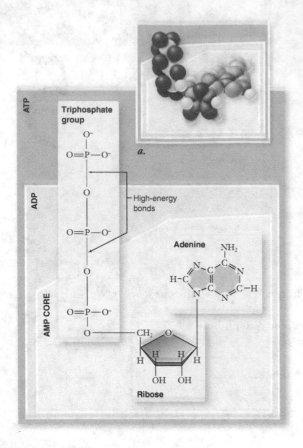

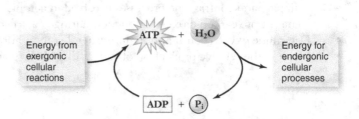

Figure 5.1

(a) ATP structure; (b) The hydrolysis and dehydration synthesis reactions involving ATP.

The process of cellular respiration (Figure 5.4) can be subdivided into four stages:

(1) **Glycolysis**,
(2) **Pyruvate oxidation**,
(3) the **Kreb's cycle** and
(4) the **Electron Transport Chain and Chemiosmosis**.

Glycolysis takes places in the cytoplasm and begins by priming glucose in preparation for splitting each molecule of glucose (6 Carbon sugar) into 2 molecules of the 3 Carbon sugar phosphate, glyceraldehyde 3–phosphate (G3P). Through a series of subsequent reactions, each G3P compound is eventually converted into a pyruvate molecule, which will either enter into the Kreb's cycle in the presence of Oxygen (**aerobic respiration**) or will undergo fermentation (**anaerobic respiration**) if Oxygen is absent. Glycolysis yields a total of 4 ATP molecules, however, 2 ATP are used during the priming reactions leading up to the splitting of glucose, thus a net of 2 ATP are produced for the entire process. Glycolysis, as a result of using the enzyme G3P Dehydrogenase and Redox reactions, also yields 2 NADH coenzyme molecules.

During the next stage, if Oxygen is present, the pyruvate generated from glycolysis enters the mitochondria from the cytoplasm, where it is converted to Acetyl Coenzyme A (Acetyl CoA). Through the use of a multi-enzyme complex a decarboxylation (loss of CO_2) event occurs, coupled with a Redox reaction, which leads to the reduction of NAD^+ to NADH. The final step in the reaction is the addition of the Coenzyme A, via oxidation, to the remaining organic molecule, essentially an acetyl group, which yields Acetyl CoA. For every 1 glucose molecule that enter glycolysis there are 2 pyruvate molecules that result. Both of these pyruvate molecules are converted into Acetyl CoA. Thus, when considering pyruvate oxidation there are two series of reactions, not just one, that occur for every glucose molecule that enters glycolysis. The yield of products for pyruvate oxidation includes 2 Acetyl Coenzyme A, 2 CO_2, and 2 NADH.

Acetyl Coenzyme A then interacts with a 4 Carbon molecule, oxaloacetate, in the mitochondrial matrix. Since there are 2 Acetyl Coenzyme A molecules produced for every 1 molecule of glucose entering this biochemical pathway,

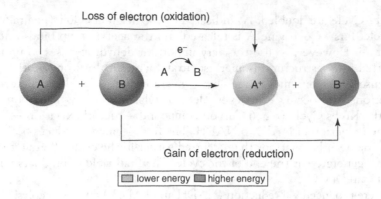

Figure 5.2

Oxidation-Reduction Reaction.

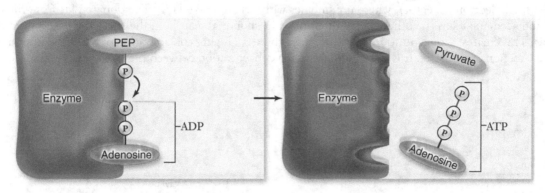

Figure 5.3

Substrate-Level Phosphorylation.

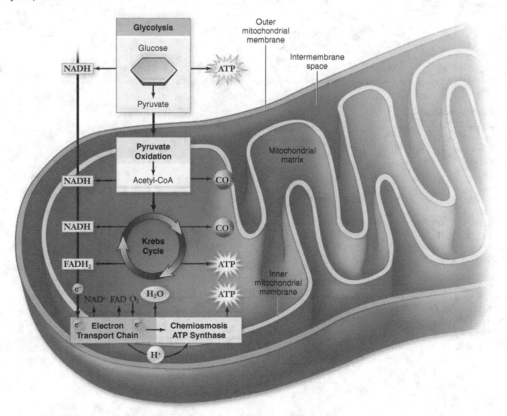

Figure 5.4

An Overview of Aerobic Respiration.

all the products of the Krebs Cycle are doubled. As indicated by the diagram below (Figure 5.5), there are three general segments to the Krebs Cycle. First, Coenzyme A is released and the acetyl group binds onto oxaloacetate, to make a 6 Carbon compound, Citrate. However, to use the very important dehydrogenases to undergo the Redox reactions, Citrate needs to be converted into a structural isomer, Isocitrate; without this isomerization event the proper substrate would not be available for use by the enzymes in the next segment of the cycle. Next, there are 2 decarboxylations (loss of CO_2) and 2 redox reactions that occur. With every decarboxylation there is 1 Carbon that is lost from the main organic molecule used in the Krebs Cycle (e.g. 6 Carbon compound → decarboxylation → 5 Carbon compound). The redox reaction results in the reduction of NAD^+ to NADH. The final segment produces both NADH and another coenzyme $FADH_2$. In addition, the decarboxylations that occurred earlier in the cycle allows for the original 4 Carbon compound, oxaloacetate, to be regenerated at the end of the cycle. The final yield of products for the Krebs Cycle includes: 2 ATP, 2 $FADH_2$, 6 NADH, and 4 CO_2.

The coenzymes that were produced via reduction (NADH and $FADH_2$) during glycolysis, pyruvate oxidation, and the Krebs Cycle are now used in the Electron Transport Chain (ETC), on the Inner mitochondrial membrane. Both NADH and $FADH_2$ donate electrons and Hydrogen (H^+). The electrons are passed through the enzymes in the ETC until it interacts with Oxygen (the final electron acceptor), where it combines with $2H^+$ to make H_2O. The donated H^+ from the coenzymes get transferred and accumulate on the other side of the Inner mitochondrial matrix, in the Mitochondrial Intermembrane space (Figure 5.6a). This creates a concentration gradient, where there is a higher concentration of H^+ in the Intermembrane space, than in the Mitochondrial Matrix. It is this difference in ion concentration between the Intermembrane space and the matrix

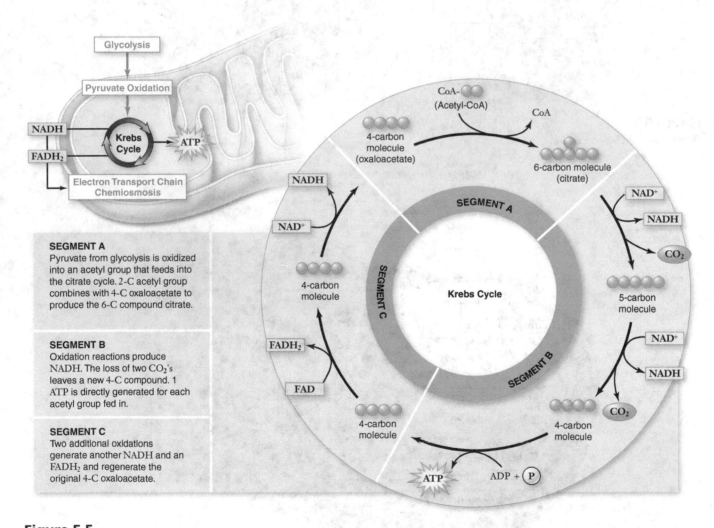

SEGMENT A
Pyruvate from glycolysis is oxidized into an acetyl group that feeds into the citrate cycle. 2-C acetyl group combines with 4-C oxaloacetate to produce the 6-C compound citrate.

SEGMENT B
Oxidation reactions produce NADH. The loss of two CO_2's leaves a new 4-C compound. 1 ATP is directly generated for each acetyl group fed in.

SEGMENT C
Two additional oxidations generate another NADH and an $FADH_2$ and regenerate the original 4-C oxaloacetate.

Figure 5.5

The Krebs Cycle.

that powers the synthesis of ATP via oxidative phosphorylation or chemiosmosis. The proton motor force drives the rotary engine, ATP Synthase (Figure 5.6b), to make energy. This is the most efficient method of making ATP. This process alone yields approximately 32 ATP.

All living organisms respire, but to some organisms Oxygen is either toxic or not readily available for cells to use to make energy. These organisms had to evolve an alternative method of producing ATP. Oxygen in aerobic respiration is used as the final electron acceptor. In some anaerobic systems, an organic compound is used as the final electron acceptor, instead of Oxygen. There are a few other options for final electron acceptors seen among living organisms, such as in Methanogens (CO_2) and Sulfur Bacteria (SO_4). There are two main types of fermentation (anaerobic respiration with organic compounds): Ethanol and Lactic Acid Fermentation. Ethanol fermentation occurs in organisms like yeast, and we use this alternative pathway industrially to produce alcohol. Lactic Acid fermentation occurs in animal cells. When oxygen is not readily available to our muscle tissue, for instance, we revert to plan B—Lactic Acid Fermentation. Lactic Acid is what is being produced when you go to the gym and your muscle start to sting. The net yield of ATP that results through this process is formed during glycolysis (net yield of 2 ATP). All organisms undergo glycolysis, which indicates that the evolution of this pathway occurred early on in the evolutionary line. Once pyruvate is made at the end of glycolysis is when the decision is made to either go into aerobic or anaerobic respiration. If oxygen is present pyruvate is converted into Acetyl CoA and moves into the Krebs Cycle. If oxygen is not present, then an organic molecule needs to serve as the final electron acceptor. Since, the steps involved in fermentation do not make more ATP than what was already made during glycolysis, the main point of having these extra steps is to (1) recycle NADH back into NAD^+ and (2) to have somewhere for the electrons from NADH to end up after it is converted back into NAD^+. During aerobic respiration, the recycling of NADH back into NAD^+ occurs when NADH is oxidized into NAD^+ in the Electron Transport Chain (Figure 5.7).

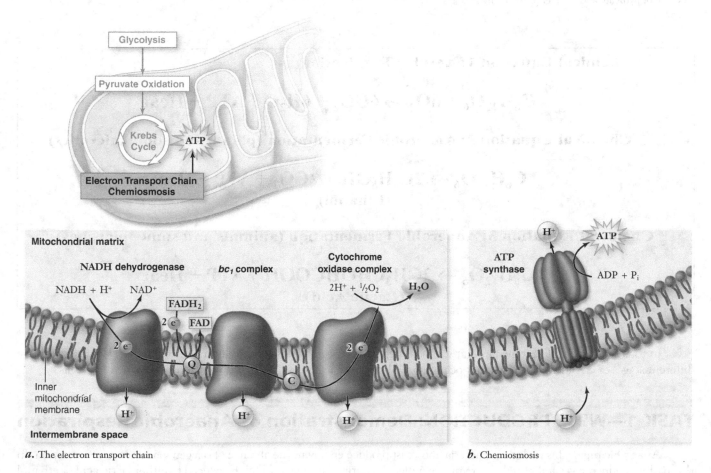

a. The electron transport chain

b. Chemiosmosis

Figure 5.6
(a) Electron Transport Chain; (b) Chemiosmosis.

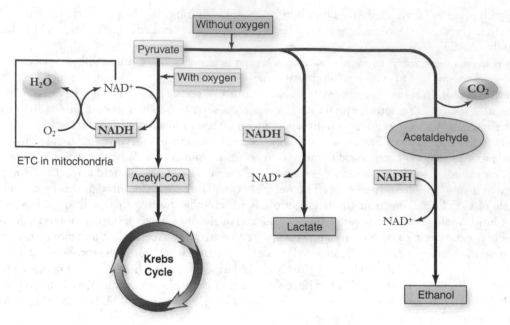

Figure 5.7

The fate of pyruvate and NADH produced by glycolysis.

Chemical Equation 1: Aerobic Respiration

$$C_6H_{12}O_6 + 6O_2 \rightarrow 6CO_2 + 6H_2O + ATP + Heat$$

Chemical Equation 2: Anaerobic Fermentation (plants and some microbes)

$$C_6H_{12}O_6 \rightarrow 2C_2H_5OH + 2CO_2 + ATP + Heat$$
$$\text{(Ethanol)}$$

Chemical Equation 3: Anaerobic Fermentation (animals and some microbes)

$$C_6H_{12}O_6 \rightarrow 2CH_3CHOHCOOH + ATP + Heat$$
$$\text{(Lactic Acid)}$$

In today's lab we will become familiar with the step by step processes that occur during respiration and demonstrate the different stages or chemical processes that occur during both aerobic and anaerobic respiration using living organisms.

TASK 1—WINE PRODUCTION: Demonstration of Anaerobic Respiration

Anaerobic organisms including bacteria and yeast produce energy in the absence of oxygen via anaerobic respiration. In this pathway, glucose is catabolized to 2 pyruvate molecules during glycolysis, which is reduced to either lactic acid or ethanol and CO_2 during fermentation. In this exercise you will demonstrate CO_2 production during anaerobic fermentation by yeast through the production of wine.

Procedure 5.1

I. Preparation of Yeast-Grape Juice Mixture by the instructor

1. Add 2 L of grape juice concentrate to an Erlenmeyer flask and allow it come to room temperature. Dilute the grape concentrate in water. Make sure the total solution is 2 L.

2. To a 20 mL beaker add 4 mL of **tap** water. Heat the beaker of water to 40–43 ^{0}C using a hot plate. **Note:** Distilled or deionized water is lethal to yeast. Make sure that you only use **tap** water.

3. Once the water is at 40–43 ^{0}C, move the beaker to the corner of the hot plate so that the water remains at the required temperature.

4. Add 0.4 g of yeast to the heated tap water. Leave the yeast-water mixture undisturbed for 15 min. You should begin to see bubbles form as the yeast re-hydrates.

5. At the end of the 15 min period, mix the yeast-water solution thoroughly and then pour it into the flask containing the grape juice. To ensure that all the yeast is added to the grape juice, pour about 15 mL of the grape juice into the beaker that contained the yeast-water mixture, stir gently, and then pour the contents back into the flask containing the yeast-grape juice solution. Mix well using a stir bar.

II. Experimental Setup

1. Label the 500 mL Erlenmeyer flask with your instructor's name, section number, group number, sucrose concentration (see step 2) and today's date.

2. Your instructor will assign each group a different amount of sucrose (0, 25 g, 55 g, 85 g, 115 g, 150 g) to add to your flask. Weigh out the group's assigned amount of sucrose (using a weighing boat) and then pour it into your group's flask using a funnel.

3. Measure 325 mL of the yeast-grape juice mixture and then add it to the flask.

4. Dissolve the sucrose in the yeast-grape juice solution by whirling the flask or using a glass rod to stir.

5. Measure 10 mL of the yeast-grape juice mixture with a pipette and add it into a small tasting cup. Set it aside. **YOU WILL NEED IT TO PERFORM THE ALCOHOL DETERMINATION PROCEDURE BELOW. PERFORM THIS PROCEDURE NOW, THEN RETURN TO THE FOLLOWING STEP (STEP 6).**

6. Attach a balloon to the opening of the flask and secure it with a rubber band.

7. Measure the circumference of the balloon by recording the distance required to wrap the measuring tape around the widest section of the balloon. Make sure to mark the balloon indicating where you measured the circumference. This will serve as your day 0 measurement and should be recorded in Table 5.1.

8. Using the previously set aside yeast-grape juice solution to measure the mass of the solution, have one member of your group take a small sip and note its sweetness (See Monitoring/measuring fermentation instructions below) in Table 5.2. Make sure you finished the alcohol determination procedure BEFORE taking a sip.

9. Over the next two lab periods (days 7 and 14), you will monitor your group's flask and record your results in Table 5.1.

- **Note:** Make sure to share your results with the remainder of the class in order to be able to graph the class data for each treatment.

Given what you know about anaerobic respiration, formulate hypotheses (Scientific, H_o and H_a) for what you expect to occur to the circumference of the balloons at the different sugar concentrations (**Hint:** consider the products of anaerobic respiration). Write the hypotheses in the space provided and explain your reasoning where appropriate.

Scientific:

H_o:

H_a:

Given what you know about anaerobic respiration, formulate hypotheses (Scientific, H_o and H_a) for what you expect to occur to the <u>percentage of alcohol</u> at the different sugar concentrations (**Hint:** consider the products of anaerobic respiration). Write the hypotheses in the space provided and explain your reasoning where appropriate.

Scientific:

H_o:

H_a:

TABLE 5.1

PREDICTIONS-WINE PRODUCTION

Dissolved Mass of sucrose (g)	Day 14			
	% alcohol (relative)	presence of sediment	presence of bubbles	CO_2 levels = balloon circumference
0				
25				
55				
85				
115				
150				

TABLE 5.2

PROVIDE THE REASONING FOR YOUR PREDICTIONS IN TABLE 5.1

Dissolved Mass of sucrose (g)	Day 14
	Reasoning
0	
25	
55	
85	
115	
150	

Monitoring/Measuring Fermentation

- Table 5.3
  - Presence/absence of bubbles produced
  - Presence/absence of sediment (deposit formed at the bottom of the flask)
  - Circumference of the balloon for your group's flask using the tape measure.

TABLE 5.3
RESULTS

Dissolved Mass of sucrose (g)	Day 0			Day 14		
	presence of bubbles	CO₂ levels = Balloon circumference	presence of sediment	presence of bubbles	CO₂ levels = Balloon circumference	presence of sediment
0						
25						
55						
85						
115						
150						

Determining Alcohol Content of Wine

When sugar is added to grape juice, the addition of mass, with a higher density than water, increases the density of the liquid. A greater density then translates into a larger specific gravity. Specific gravity is the density of the liquid divided by the density of water (0.998 g/mL).

$$SG = \frac{Density\ of\ Solution}{Density\ of\ Water}$$

Equation 1. Specific gravity of a solution is determined by the quotient of the density of the solution and water.

When yeast undergoes fermentation to produce wine, they utilize the sugar and produce ethanol. The removal of the denser mass (sugar) decreases the density the density of the liquid. The production of ethanol also lowers the density because ethanol has a lesser density than water. These changes in density cause the specific gravity of the grape juice to be lowered. The change in specific gravity can be used to determine the amount of alcohol produced.

$$\%\ Alcohol = \frac{SG_I - SG_F}{0.00736}$$

Equation 2. The percentage of alcohol in grape juice determined by changes in specific gravity.
Divide the difference between the initial specific gravity (SG_I) and the final specific gravity (SG_F) by 0.00736.

Complete the table below (Table 5.4) to determine the initial specific gravity of the solution. This step should be performed once the grape juice and the appropriate amount of sucrose have been mixed in your Erlenmeyer flask. Once this procedure has been completed cover the opening of your flask with the balloon.

Procedure 5.2

1. Measure 10 mL of the grape juice solution.
2. Using a balance measure the mass of the solution.
3. Use the equations above to calculate the Initial Specific Gravity.

TABLE 5.4

INITIAL SPECIFIC GRAVITY OF GRAPE JUICE AT DIFFERING SUCROSE CONCENTRATIONS

Sucrose (g)	Mass of 10 mL (g)	Density of Wine (g/mL)	Initial Specific Gravity (SGI)
0			
25			
55			
85			
115			
150			

On day 14 of the experiment after the final circumference of the balloon has been measured, complete the table below (Table 2) to determine alcohol content in the different wines fermented in your lab.

TABLE 5.5

ALCOHOL CONTENT PRODUCED BY GRAPE JUICE WITH DIFFERING SUCROSE CONCENTRATIONS

Sucrose (g)	Mass of 10 mL (g)	Density of Wine (g/mL)	Final Specific Gravity (SGF)	Alcohol Content (%)
0				
25				
55				
85				
115				
150				

Questions

1. Which of the variables is (are) the independent variable(s)?

2. Which of the variables is (are) the dependent variable(s)?

3. What variables serve as controls and what do they control for?

4. Was there a noticeable increase in the number of bubbles and/or presence of sediment for all treatments over time?

TABLE 5.6

TASTE THE WINE ON DAYS 0 AND 14. ON A SCALE OF 0–6, WITH 6 BEING VERY SWEET AND 0, NOT SWEET AT ALL; COMPARE THE SWEETNESS OF THE SOLUTIONS

Dissolved Mass of Sucrose (g)	Taste Observation (0–6)	
	Day 0	Day 14
0		
25		
55		
85		
115		
150		

5. What happened to the balloon circumference of each flask as the fermentation process progressed?

6. How does balloon circumference relate to the amount of carbon dioxide produced during fermentation?

7. What happens to CO_2 levels with increasing sugar concentration? Is this pattern observed for all sucrose treatments?

8. Based on your results, can you explain which ingredients are essential for fermentation to occur and why?

9. Did your observed results reflect your predictions for the circumference of the balloon?

10. Do you reject or fail to reject your null hypothesis for the circumference of the balloon? Explain.

11. Did your observed results reflect your predictions for the percentage of alcohol?

12. Do you reject or fail to reject your null hypothesis for the percentage of alcohol? Explain.

13. Identify any possible sources of error which may have affected the results of this experiment.

14. Using excel, make a bar graph with the results of the circumference of the balloons and the percentage of alcohol side by side.

15. Compare the amount of alcohol produced to the results obtained for balloon circumference. Is there a trend? Explain.

TASK 2—DEMONSTRATION OF AEROBIC RESPIRATION: Consumption of O_2

In this task you will examine aerobic respiration by measuring the amount of oxygen consumed by germinating and dormant (heat-killed) peas. In addition, you will assess the effect of temperature on the rate of aerobic respiration by performing the experiment at two different temperatures.

Given what you know about aerobic respiration, formulate hypotheses (H_o and H_a) for what you expect to occur to the respiration rates in germinating v. dormant peas. Write the hypotheses in the space provided and explain your reasoning where appropriate.

Scientific:

H_o:

H_a:

Given what you know about aerobic respiration, formulate hypotheses (Scientific, H_o and H_a) for what you expect to occur to the <u>respiration rates in germinating v. dormant peas when exposed to different temperatures</u>. Write the hypotheses in the space provided and explain your reasoning where appropriate.

Room Temperature bath:

Scientific:

H_o:

H_a:

Ice bath:

Scientific:

H_o:

H_a:

Procedure 5.3

1. Your instructor will assign half of the class to perform the experiment in freezing conditions and the other half at room temperature. Depending on your assignment, your group will need to either setup an ice water bath or a room temperature water bath. Once this has been done, record the temperature of your group's water bath in the space provided below.

Water Bath Temp: _____°C

2. Set up three respirometers as shown in Figure 5.8.

    Do <u>NOT</u> touch KOH with your bare hands, it is very caustic! Please use gloves and a spatula when working with KOH.

Tube 1: Place a small amount of absorbent cotton at the bottom of the tube followed by 5 g **germinating** peas, another small plug of cotton, and then approximately 1 cm of *KOH pellets. Place a rubber stopper with a glass pipette in the top of the tube and then completely cover with foil.

Tube 2: Place a small amount of cotton at the bottom of the tube followed by 5 g **dormant (heat-killed)** peas, another small plug of cotton, and then approximately 1 cm of *KOH pellets. Place a rubber stopper with a glass pipette in the top of the tube and then completely cover with foil.

Tube 3: Place a small amount of cotton at the bottom of the tube followed by 5 g **beads**, another small plug of cotton, and then approximately 1 cm of *KOH pellets. Place a rubber stopper with a glass pipette in the top of the tube and then completely cover with foil.

*KOH (potassium hydroxide) absorbs the CO_2 produced during aerobic respiration.

3. Place all three tubes in the water bath (Figure 5.9). The tubes should be submerged in water/ice at least ¾ of the way up to the stopper. Allow the tubes to equilibrate at this temperature for 10 minutes.

4. Add 1 drop of colored dye (toluidine blue) using a transfer pipette into the tip of each of the three respirometers making sure not to lift the tubes out of the water bath. MAKE SURE TO KEEP THE TEMPERATURE CONSTANT THROUGHOUT THE EXPERIMENT.

5. Allow the tubes to equilibrate for 5 min and then record the temperature of the water bath as well as the initial location of the dye in the corresponding table below. DO NOT MOVE THE WATER BATH OR THE TABLE.

6. Record the water bath temperature as well as dye location for each tube every 10 min (Total time = 30 min). Make sure to also record the results obtained by a neighboring group for a different temperature treatment.

Figure 5.8
Respirometer Setup: 1-germinating peas, 2-heat killed peas, 3-beads.

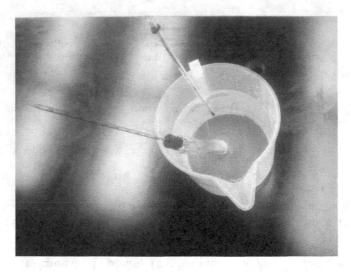

Figure 5.9
Water bath setup showing respirometers (view from the top).

Predictions

TABLE 5.7

ICE WATER BATH PREDICTIONS

Tube #	Relative respiration rate	Reasoning
Tube 1		
Tube 2		
Tube 3		

TABLE 5.8

ROOM TEMPERATURE PREDICTIONS

Tube #	Relative respiration rate	Reasoning
Tube 1		
Tube 2		
Tube 3		

TABLE 5.9

ICE WATER BATH RESULTS

Time (min)	Temp of water bath (°C)	Tube 1 respirometer reading (mm)	Tube 2 respirometer reading (mm)	Tube 3 respirometer reading (mm)
0				
10				
20				
30				

TABLE 5.10

ROOM TEMPERATURE WATER BATH RESULTS

Time (min)	Temp of water bath (°C)	Tube 1 respirometer reading (mm)	Tube 2 respirometer reading (mm)	Tube 3 respirometer reading (mm)
0				
10				
20				
30				

Questions

16. Which of the variables is (are) the independent variable(s)?

17. Which of the variables is (are) the dependent variable(s)?

18. What variables serve as controls and what do they control for?

19. Using Excel, plot 2 graphs: one for the results of each of the three tubes in the ice water bath (Table 5.9) and the other for each of the three tubes in the room temperature water bath (Table 5.10).

20. What was the purpose of using KOH pellets? What would have happened to our results had we not used them?

21. Based on your results (look at your graphs), which was relatively faster, the germinating peas or heat-killed peas? Why?

22. How did temperature affect respiratory rate? Why do you think temperature affected or did not affect this rate?

23. Explain how this experiment demonstrated oxygen consumption as a part of cellular respiration.

24. Explain the effects of germination (versus non-germination) on pea seed respiration.

25. Did your observed results reflect your predictions?

26. Do you reject or fail to reject your null hypothesis? Explain.

27. If you used the same experimental design to compare the rates of respiration of a 25 g mammal at 10 ^{0}C, what results would you expect? Explain your reasoning.

TASK 3—DEMONSTRATION OF AEROBIC RESPIRATION: Production of CO_2

When eukaryotic organisms respire they release CO_2 which can combine with H_2O to form carbonic acid (H_2CO_3). In general, acidic solutions such as H_2CO_3 (pH less than 7) have a larger concentration of H^+ ions while basic ones (pH greater than 7) contain more OH^- ions (Figure 5.10). An indicator, such as phenolphthalein can be used to detect changes in pH resulting from CO_2 production during cellular respiration. In an acidic solution, phenolphthalein is clear, but in basic solutions it turns pink.

Metabolic rate is not constant in any given organism. Any bodily process that requires energy will raise the organism's metabolic rate, which will increase the organism's need for oxygen. Environmental factors can alter an organism's metabolic rate as well. Using crayfish as the model organism aerobic respiration by measuring the volume of NaOH required to neutralize the acid produced by actively respiring crayfish.

Considering the set-up for this procedure (Table 5.11), state what you expect to occur when comparing respiratory rates at different temperatures. Write the hypotheses in the space provided and explain your reasoning where appropriate.

Scientific:

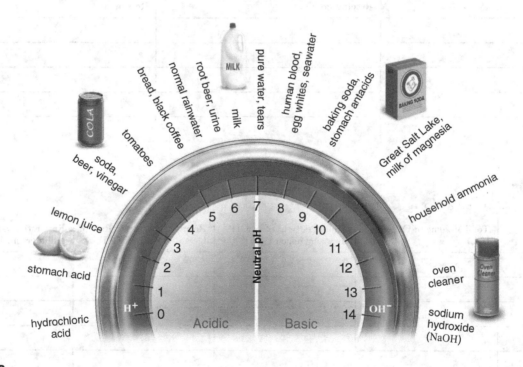

Figure 5.10
pH Scale.

H_o:

H_a:

Procedure 5.4

Caution: Crayfish can survive out of the water for several minutes; however, it is not ideal for the purposes of this experiment to add dehydration stress. This can negatively affect your respiration rate results. Avoid holding the crayfish out of the water for any extended period of time. Place them immediately back in the water.

1. At the lab bench there should be a small crayfish testing chamber as well as a pan of water that has been treated and aerated. To start the room temperature measurements, fill the testing chamber completely with the aerated water.

2. Set the holding pen in a pan with about 2 cm of room temperature water.
3. Remove the crayfish from the small crayfish tank. Weigh it and measure its volume through volume displacement.
4. Place the crayfish gently into the testing chamber.
5. Allow a 5 minute acclimation period before taking the time zero measurement using the pH meter.
6. Take readings of the pH changes at 5 minute intervals until the 20 minute mark.
7. Remove the small crayfish from the testing chamber and place the crayfish back into the tank.
8. Repeat each of the above steps for each treatment listed in Table 5.11.
9. DO NOT ADD THE INDICATOR UNTIL YOU HAVE TAKEN THE ORGANISMS OUT OF THE BEAKERS. Add 4 drops of phenolphthalein to each beaker. The contents should remain clear because the solutions are acidic.
10. Place the pH meter into the water to aid in the determination of the endpoint.
11. Add NaOH drop by drop to the contents of the control beaker to determine the number of drops it takes to turn the solution pink (20 drops = 1 mL). After each drop thoroughly mix the contents of the beaker.
12. Record your results in Table 5.12.
13. Repeat steps 9–12 for each of the remaining beakers.

TABLE 5.11

Treatment	Respiration Rate	Reasoning
Small, 22°C		
Large, 22°C		
Small, 32°C		
Large, 32°C		
0.4% Salinity, 22°C		

TABLE 5.12

RESULTS AND CALCULATIONS

Treatment	Total Volume of Organisms (mL)	Milliliters (mL) of NaOH to reach endpoint	Relative Respiration Rate of Organisms (mL NaOH)	Respiration rate per milliliter (mL) of organism
Small, 22°C				
Large, 22°C				
Small, 32°C				
Large, 32°C				
0.4% Salinity, 22°C				
Control				

PREDICTIONS

To calculate the relative respiration rate of each organism, subtract mL NaOH added to the control beaker from the milliliters added to each beaker. Record your results in Table 5.12.

Calculations:

To determine the respiration rate per milliliter of organism, divide the relative respiration rate by the volume of each organism. Record your results in Table 5.12.

Calculations:

Questions

28. Which of the variables is (are) the independent variable(s)?

29. Which of the variables is (are) the dependent variable(s)?

30. What variables serve as controls and what do they control for?

31. What major energy producing process is characteristic of plant cells but not animal cells?

32. What gas is consumed in this process?

33. What was the purpose of including the 6th setup (control)?

34. Using the data collected from this experiment, what can you conclude about respiratory rates in small versus large crayfish?

35. Using the data collected from this experiment, what can you conclude about respiratory rates in crayfish exposed to high salt concentrations?

36. Using the data collected from this experiment, what can you conclude about respiratory rates in crayfish exposed to high temperatures versus low temperatures?

37. What possible sources of error are associated with this procedure?

38. Did your observed results reflect your predictions?

39. Do you reject or fail to reject your null hypothesis? Explain.

Mitosis and the Cell Cycle

6

Objectives

- Differentiate between prokaryotic and eukaryotic cell division.
- Understand the major events involved in the cell cycle.
- Learn about the process of cellular division in plant and animal cells.
- Understand the major events involved in Mitosis.
- Learn about the major structural components of the chromosome.

Task 1—BINARY FISSION

Binary fission (Figure 6.1) is the process used by most prokaryotes for asexual reproduction. This process replicates the original cell, to produce two identical daughter cells. Binary fission begins with DNA replication. DNA replication starts from an origin of replication, which opens up in a bidirectional manner. Unlike eukaryotes which have multiple points of origin for replication, prokaryotic DNA replication has one origin of replication. Each strand acts as a template for synthesis via semi-conservative replication, until the entire prokaryotic DNA is duplicated. Once DNA replication has been completed each circular DNA strand will attach to the plasma membrane. Near the site of attachment, the cell elongates causing the two duplicated chromosomes to separate. Cellular division in bacteria is controlled by the FtsZ proteins, proteins that collect around the site of septation, in the middle of the cell. At this site, the FtsZ proteins regulate the assembly of the division septum. The cell wall and plasma membrane start growing diagonally close to the middle of the dividing cell. At this point, the membrane pinches inward toward the middle of the cell; when it reaches the middle, the cell splits into two daughter cells.

The population of organisms that reproduce through binary fission, provided adequate nutrients, can multiply into the billions very quickly. With a reasonably fast life cycle these populations see quick exponential growth.

It is common that one of the resultant daughter cells is not identical to the mother due to the relatively high mutation rate of bacteria. This tendency to change is what makes bacteria develop resistance to antibiotics, and what enables them to rapidly adjust to different environments.

Bacterial population growth studies require inoculation of viable cells into a sterile nutrient broth and the incubation of the bacterial culture under adequate environmental conditions: temperature, pH, and gaseous conditions. Assuming that the culture is in proper growing conditions, the bacteria will quickly divide and the changes in population size can be recorded in a population growth curve. This growth curve is made by plotting the increase in the number of bacterial cells against incubation time. Within this curve there are four stages that can be distinctly identified: (1) Lag, (2) Log, (3) Stationary, and (4) Decline phases. The growth curve can be used to facilitate the calculation of population sizes and the rate in which bacterial populations grow, a bacterium's generation time - the time required for a bacterial population to double in size.

1. **Lag phase:** During this stage the cells are adjusting to the new environment. A cellular metabolism is accelerated, resulting in rapid biosynthesis of cellular macromolecules, primarily enzymes. Although the cells are cells are moderately increasing in size, there is limited cell division and therefore only a moderate increase in cell numbers.

2. **Logarithmic (log or exponential) phase:** In the logarithmic phase the physiologically robust cells reproduce at a uniform and rapid rate by binary fission. Thus, there is a rapid exponential increase in population, which doubles regularly until a maximum number of cells is reached. The time required for the population to double is the generation time. The length of the log phase varies, depending on the organisms and the composition of the medium.

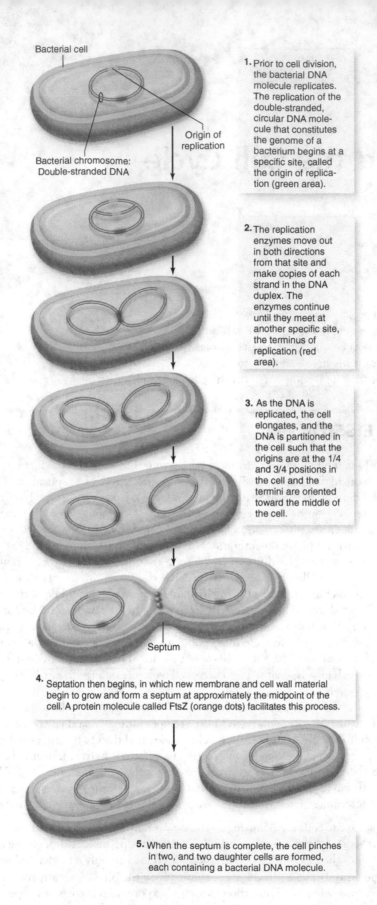

Bacterial cell

Origin of replication

Bacterial chromosome: Double-stranded DNA

1. Prior to cell division, the bacterial DNA molecule replicates. The replication of the double-stranded, circular DNA molecule that constitutes the genome of a bacterium begins at a specific site, called the origin of replication (green area).

2. The replication enzymes move out in both directions from that site and make copies of each strand in the DNA duplex. The enzymes continue until they meet at another specific site, the terminus of replication (red area).

3. As the DNA is replicated, the cell elongates, and the DNA is partitioned in the cell such that the origins are at the 1/4 and 3/4 positions in the cell and the termini are oriented toward the middle of the cell.

Septum

4. Septation then begins, in which new membrane and cell wall material begin to grow and form a septum at approximately the midpoint of the cell. A protein molecule called FtsZ (orange dots) facilitates this process.

5. When the septum is complete, the cell pinches in two, and two daughter cells are formed, each containing a bacterial DNA molecule.

Figure 6.1

Binary fission.

3. **Stationary phase:** During this stage, the number of cells undergoing division is equal to the number of cells that are dying. Therefore there is no further increase in cell number, and the population is maintained at is maximum level for a period of time. The primary factors responsible for this phase are the depletion of some essential nutrients and the accumulation of toxic acidic or alkaline waste products in the medium.

4. **Decline, or death, phase:** Because of the continuing depletion of nutrients and buildup of metabolic wastes, the microorganisms die at a rapid and uniform rate. The decrease in population closely parallels its increase during the log phase. Theoretically, the entire population should die during a time interval equal to that of the log phase. This does not occur, however, since a small number of highly resistant organisms persist for an indeterminate length of time. Construction of a complete bacterial growth curve requires that aliquots of a 24-hour shaking culture be measured for population size at intervals during the incubation period. Such a procedure does not lend itself to a regular laboratory session. Therefore, this experiment follows a modified procedure designed to demonstrate only the lag and log phases. The curve will be plotted by using an indirect method for measuring growth. The indirect method is based on spectrophotometric analysis.

In liquid culture, the medium appears cloudier as the bacteria increase in number by cell division. A tube of bacteria will tend to reflect light so that less light is transmitted through the tube. A spectrophotometer can measure the amount of light passing through the tube, or conversely the amount of light absorbed. These measurements of turbidity or optical density (OD) are not direct measurements of bacterial numbers, but an indirect measurement of cell biomass that includes both living and dead cells. You will determine generation time of cultures growing under variable conditions with the indirect spectrophotometric method by using data on the growth curve. Indirect determination is made by simple extrapolation from the log phase. Select two points on the absorbance scale (y-axis), such as 0.2 and 0.4, that represent a doubling of turbidity. Using a ruler, extrapolate by drawing a line between each of the selected absorbencies on the y-axis and the growth curve. Then draw perpendicular lines from these endpoints on the plotted line of the growth curve to their respective time intervals on the x-axis. With this information, determine the generation (GT, also called doubling time) as follows:

$$GT = t(A \text{ at } 0.4) - t(A \text{ at } 0.2)$$
$$\text{e.g. } GT = 90 \text{ minutes} - 60 \text{ minutes} = 30 \text{ minutes}$$

Based on what you know about bacterial growth, formulate hypotheses (Scientific, H_o and H_a) for what you expect to occur at the different treatments over time. Write the hypotheses in the space provided and explain your reasoning for each.

Scientific:

H_o:

H_a:

TABLE 6.1

PREDICTIONS

	Relative growth	Explanation
LB, 37 °C		
LB, Alkaline		
LB, Acidic		
LB, 45 °C		
LB, 25 °C		
LB, 2% Salinity		

Procedure A

1. With a sterile serological pipette, add 50 mL of the log phase E. *coli* culture to the flask containing 100 mL of LB broth. Swirl the flask so there is an even suspension of bacteria. Take the initial absorbance of this culture using the spectrophotometer at 600 nm using 3 mL of inoculated broth as follows:

   a. Set the wavelength to 600 nm.

   b. Blank the spectrophotometer with a cuvette containing 3 mL of uninoculated LB broth (why this?).

   c. Read the absorbance of the culture.

   The approximate initial absorbance A (t_0) should be 0.08 to 0.1 at 600 nm.

2. Place the culture flask in the incubator or on the counter, depending on the treatment, and time for the required 20-minute intervals.

3. Every 20 minutes, aseptically transfer 3 mL of the culture to a cuvette and determine its absorbance. Try to remove your 3 mL aliquots as quickly as possible to avoid cooling the culture.

TABLE 6.2

RESULTS

	Blank	0 minutes	20 minutes	40 minutes	60 minutes	75 minutes
LB, 37 °C						
LB, Alkaline						
LB, Acidic						
LB, 45 °C						
LB, 25 °C						
LB, 2% Salinity						

Using the computer program Excel, plot a bacterial growth curve with the absorbances on the y-axis and the incubation time on the x-axis. Draw the best line connecting the plotted points. On the graph identify each phase of bacterial grow. Briefly, in your words, explain what is occurring in each phase (write this directly onto the graph).

Questions

1. Why is absorbance of the bacterial culture an indicator of cell density?

2. Why do you need to set the absorbance to zero with a "blank" cuvette?

3. What trends did you observe in this experiment?

4. Determine the optimal pH and temperature for bacterial growth. Explain your reasoning for each.

Procedure B

MAKE SURE TO WEAR GLOVES!! YOU ARE WORKING WITH BACTERIA IN THIS TASK.

1. Make sure the cell plate is at about room temperature to ensure that the cells are not dormant from being in the refrigerator. Using a plastic sterile loop, transfer a mass of bacteria from the starter plate onto a microscope slide. Make sure not to clump the mass in one spot (you won't be able to see the bacteria properly).

2. Add 1 drop of methylene blue to the slide.

3. Add a coverslip. Using a kim-wipe you can pick up any excess dye. Make sure to throw the kim-wipe in the Biohazardous waste. The slide itself, once the task is complete, should be discarded in the Biohazardous sharps waste container.

4. View the slide under the microscope after a couple of minutes. Draw the cells in the space provided below. Identify cells that you believe are actively dividing.

Questions

5. In your own words, describe the process of binary fission.

6. How do the two new cells compare to each other after binary fission?

7. How do the two new cells compare to the original cell?

8. Many antibiotics work by breaking apart the structural components of the cell wall at the weakest point of the bacteria's replication process. What do you think the weakest point of the process is? Explain.

The Eukaryotic Cell Cycle

All eukaryotic cells undergo a series of growth, DNA replication and division events. These events are collectively referred to as the cell cycle (Figure 6.2). The duration of the cell cycle is specific to the cell type and organism. For example, nerve cells have long cell cycles while the epithelial cells that line the Gastrointestinal Tract have very quick cycles. In general, the cell cycle consists of three phases: **Interphase, Mitosis (M)** and **Cytokinesis (C)**. The first stage, Interphase, is considered the non-dividing or growth portion of the cell cycle and is subdivided into three phases: the **Gap 1 (G_1), Synthesis (S)**, and **Gap 2 (G_2)**.

During G_1 (the normal state of a cell), the cell grows and it synthesizes enzymes, like polymerase, and several other biochemical factors vital for DNA replication during the S phase. If the cell has not been able to gather all of the need biochemical resources and grow to the appropriate size it will enter an additional phase, the Gap 0 phase (G0). This is the stage where cells that do not divide frequently are found most of the time, nerve cells, for example. In the Gap 2 phase, the cell synthesizes several different macromolecules which function to increase the cell's size and integrity, and during this phase chromatin is prepared to be condensed into chromosomes, which occurs during the M phase.

The genetic material (DNA) of all eukaryotic organisms is housed within the cell's nucleus and is passed on from generation to generation. While a cell is in interphase, the DNA exists in an extended form called **chromatin** (Fig. 2) that repeatedly folds on top of itself, condensing into visible chromosomes when the cell is ready to divide (*i.e.*, entering the M phase of the cell cycle). In somatic (non-sex) cells, chromosomes exist in pairs and are called **homologous chromosomes**. Each homologue within the pair is referred to as a **sister chromatid** and is joined to the other by the centromere (Fig. 3). In eukaryotic organisms, the number of chromosomes present differs between species but most eukaryotes are **diploid (2n)**, meaning they have 2 pairs of chromosomes. Chromosome number differs between organisms (Table 1), for example human cells possess a total of 46 chromosomes (23 pairs), while canine cells possess a much larger number (39 pairs).

The cell cycle is controlled by a series of checkpoints (Figure 6.2), the G1/S, G2/M and spindle checkpoints. The **G1/S checkpoint**, determines if the cell should continue into the S phase directly from the Gap 1 phase or if it should enter Gap 0 phase. This checkpoint is followed by the **G2/M checkpoint**, which serves as a control mechanism to prevent damaged cells from entering the M phase. At this point cells are committed to divide via mitosis. The final checkpoint occurs in the middle of the mitotic process. The role of the **spindle checkpoint** is to ensure that all chromosomes are attached to the mitotic spindle towards the end of metaphase; if any chromosome is not attached, the cell will not be able to proceed into anaphase.

In addition, DNA damage checkpoints located in G1, S and G2 ensure that DNA is not damaged before allowing the cell to proceed to mitosis. For example, the p 53 protein, which plays a key role in the G1 checkpoint, monitors the integrity of DNA during this stage. If the DNA is healthy (i.e., no mutations) **p 53** will allow the cell to progress onwards through the cell cycle. On the other hand, if p 53 detects DNA damage, then it will arrest the cell in G1 either for repair or for destruction (apoptosis: programmed cell death). If any of these checkpoints are nonfunctional or mutated, control of the cell cycle is losvt and cancer develops.

Questions

9. Interphase is sometimes referred to as a "resting stage." Why is this inaccurate?

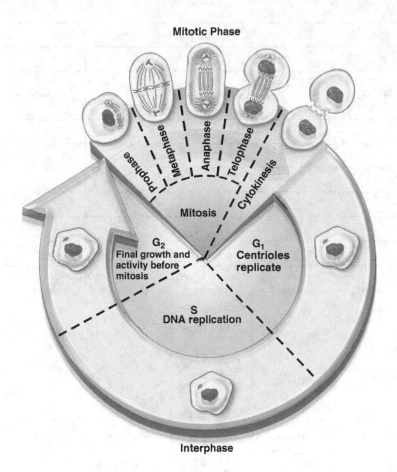

Figure 6.2
The cell cycle.

10. How might you use the knowledge of the cell cycle checkpoints to prevent, diagnose, and treat cancer?

11. What problems may occur as a result of having a mutated **p 53** protein?

Cellular Division: Mitosis

TABLE 6.3

CHROMOSOME NUMBERS

Organism	Diploid Number	Haploid Number
Jumper ant	2	1
Tapeworm	4	2
Mosquito	6	3
Housefly	12	6

Organism	Diploid Number	Haploid Number
Onion	16	8
Rice	24	12
Tomato	24	12
Cat	38	19
Human	46	23
Chimpanzee	48	24
Potato	48	24
Horse	64	32
Dog	78	39
Stalked adder's tongue fern	1,260	630

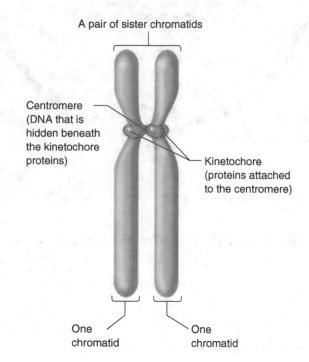

A pair of sister chromatids

Centromere (DNA that is hidden beneath the kinetochore proteins)

Kinetochore (proteins attached to the centromere)

One chromatid

One chromatid

Figure 6.3

Chromosome numbers vary across species.

Eukaryotic cells, depending on the type (somatic vs. germ cells), divide either by **mitosis** or **meiosis**. Mitosis occurs in somatic cells, which are all cells of the body excluding the reproductive cells (eggs and sperm). Mitosis is the process in which a diploid parental cell is divided into 2 identical daughter cells, also diploid in number. Germ cells undergo a different process that allows for a reduction in the ploidy number, from diploid to haploid, and a series of two divisions which are included in the process of meiosis.

Mitosis (Fig. 6.4) is a nuclear event comprised of 4 stages, Prophase, Metaphase, Anaphase and Telophase. Be aware that in several texts an intermediate stage between Prophase and Metaphase is added. Usually following nuclear division, the 2 newly generated daughter cells are separated from each other through the process of cytokinesis (division of the cytoplasm). During cytokinesis animal cells form a **cleavage furrow** or indentation on the periphery of the cell that pulls the plasma membrane inward, dividing the cell into two parts. Plant cells, in contrast, are unable to divide using the cleavage furrow since they possess a rigid cell wall. Instead, the Golgi apparatus, once it is reintroduced into the cell during Telophase, will produce vesicles that will align across the middle of the cell, which will join together to generate a cell plate dividing the plant cell into two.

(a) Interphase
- The chromosomes are in an extended form and seen as chromatin in the electron microscope.
- The nucleus is visible

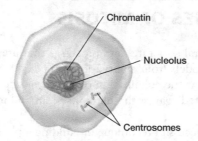
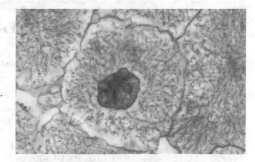

Chromatin

Nucleolus

Centrosomes

(b) Prophase
- The chromosomes are seen to consist of two chromatids joined by a centromere.
- The centrioles move apart toward opposite poles of the cell.
- Spindle fibers are produced and extend from each centrosome.
- The nuclear membrane starts to disappear.
- The nucleolus is no longer visible.

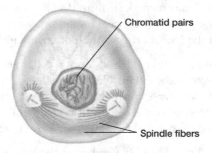

Chromatid pairs

Spindle fibers

(c) Metaphase
- The chromosomes are lined up at the equator of the cell.
- The spindle fibers from each centriole are attached to the centromeres of the chromosomes.
- The nuclear membrane has disappeared.

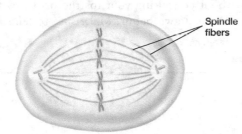
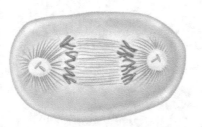
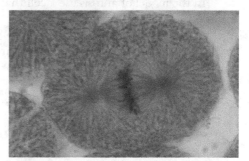

Spindle fibers

(d) Anaphase
- The centromere split, and the sister chromatids separate as each is pulled to an opposite pole.

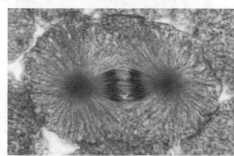
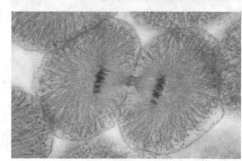

(e) Telophase
- The chromosomes become longer, thinner, and less distinct.
- New nuclear membranes form.
- The nucleolus reappears.
- Cell division is nearly complete.

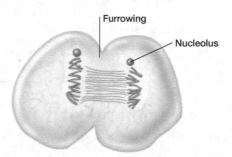

Furrowing

Nucleolus

Figure 6.4
Mitosis.

Task 2—IDENTIFY THE STAGES OF MITOSIS

Researchers use models to represent natural structures and processes that are too small, too large, or too complex to investigate directly. Scientists develop their models from observations and experimental data usually accumulated from a variety of sources. Building a model can represent the culmination of a body of scientific work, but most models represent a well-developed hypothesis that can then be tested against the natural system and modified as needed to reflect the natural system.

For instance, Linus Pauling's novel and successful technique of building a physical model of hemoglobin was based on available chemical data. This technique was later adopted by Francis Crick and James Watson to elucidate the nature of the hereditary material, DNA. Watson and Crick built a wire model utilizing evidence collected by Rosalind Franklin and several other scientists. They presented their conclusions about the three-dimensional structure of DNA, the double helix, in the journal *Nature* in April 1953 and were awarded the Nobel Prize for their discovery in 1962.

a. Today in lab you will work with your group to build models of mitotic cell division. Using these models will enhance your understanding of the behavior of chromosomes, centrioles, membranes, and microtubules during the cell cycle. After completing your model, you will consider ways in which it is and is not an appropriate model for the cell cycle. Your group should discuss activities in each stage of the cell cycle as you build your model. After going through the exercise once together, you will demonstrate the model to each other to reinforce your understanding.

In the model of mitosis use a cell that is a diploid cell (2n) with four chromosomes. One set will be long chromosomes, the other set, short chromosomes.

Do not move on to the next stage without consulting your instructor. Draw the resulting daughter cells in the space provided below. Label any structure that is drawn below. Make sure to lebel sister chromatids and homologous chromosomes.

b. Using the molecular model at the end of part A, as drawn above, go through a the cell cycle ending with a mitotic division.

c. Using the molecular model, design a model that demonstrates the results of a cell when a spindle fiber does not attach properly to the kinetochore of chromosome 3. Draw your resulting daughter cells below.

Questions

1. How many sister chromatids are you using in these models? DNA Molecules?

2. What differences do you observe between model B and C?

3. If this happened in a human what could happen to the daughter cells?

Task 3—BIOLOGICAL EXAMPLE OF CELL DIVISION

1. Examine a prepared slide of the whitefish blastula on high power.
2. Complete Table 2, making sure to draw examples of each phase of mitosis.

TABLE 6.4

Stage of Mitosis	Description of Events	Drawings of Stages
Prophase		
Metaphase		

Continued

Stage of Mitosis	Description of Events	Drawings of Stages
Anaphase		
Telophase		

Questions

4. Why are cells from a blastula ideal to examine mitosis?

5. How fast do you think cells divide when an embryo is forming compared to the normal growth of an animal?

6. Do plants have centrioles? Why is this an important fact?

7. How does cytokinesis differ between plant and animal cells?

8. What are two important changes that chromosomes must undergo before cell division can take place?

Task 4—PREPARATION OF AN ONION ROOT TIP SLIDE

1. Cut off a root tip approximately 5 mm long and place the root tip in a 1.5 mL Eppendorf tube.
2. Fill the Eppendorf tube with about 200 μL, or until the tip is completely submerged, of 6 M HCl. Allow the onion root tip to soak in the acid for 4 minutes. (MAKE SURE YOU ARE WEARING GLOVES)
3. Transfer the root tip to a second Eppendorf tube. Fill the Eppendorf tube with about 200 μL, or until the tip is completely submerged, of Carnoy's Fixative. Allow the onion root tip to soak in the fixative for 4 minutes.
4. Place the root tip onto a watch glass and using a dissecting microscope, to ensure you are cutting the correct end of the root tip, cut a 2 mm piece of the root tip. Discard the rest.
5. Take the root tip out of the watch glass and place each on the middle of a microscope slide. The slide should be placed on a paper towel.
6. Place two drops of carbol fuschin stain on top of the 2 mm root tip. Let the stain soak into the root tip for 2 minutes.
7. After 2 minutes blot away any excess stain from the slide by using a Kimwipe. Try no to disturb the root tip.
8. Add 1 drop of dH_2O to the stained onion root tip.
9. Gently place a coverslip over the onion root tip.
10. Squash the root tip pressing straight down so as not to overlap the cells. When pressing down on the slide cover the slide with a paper towel to soak up any excess stain that comes out from between the slide and the coverslip. Be careful not to twist the coverslip or to break the slide. The act of squashing separates the cells from each other, making the chromosomes more visible.

TABLE 6.5

Stage of Cell Cycle	Number of Cells					Calculation of Time Spent in Each Stage
	FOV 1	FOV 2	FOV 3	FOV 4	Total	
Interphase						
Prophase						
Metaphase						
Anaphase						
Telophase						

TABLE 6.6

Stage of Mitosis	Drawings of Stages as seen in the Onion Root Slide
Interphase	
Prophase	

Continues

6–13

Stage of Mitosis	Drawings of Stages as seen in the Onion Root Slide
Metaphase	
Anaphase	
Telophase	

Questions

9. Why are we using the onion root tip as an example of plant cellular division versus any other part of the root?

10. A cell biologist carefully measured the quantity of DNA in grasshopper cells growing in cell culture. Cells examined during the G1 phase of the cell cycle contained 200 units of DNA. What would be the amount of DNA in one of the grasshopper daughter cells right after cytokinesis?

11. A dividing cell has a line of vesicles on the metaphase plate between the two daughter nuclei. Is it a bacterium, plant, or animal cell? What are these vesicles?

Task 5—THE CHROMOSOME

A **chromosome** is an organized structure of DNA and protein found in cells. It is a single piece of coiled DNA containing many genes, regulatory elements and other nucleotide sequences. Chromosomes also contain DNA-bound proteins, which serve to package the DNA and control its functions.

Chromosomes structure and size vary between organisms. The DNA strand can be either linear or circular in shape, and can consist of 100,000 to billions of nucleotides in a linked double helical chain. Eukaryotic cells have larger linear chromosomes and prokaryotic cells have smaller circular chromosomes.

In eukaryotes, nuclear chromosomes are condensed by proteins into a compressed structure called chromatin, which allows DNA strands to fit into the nucleus. DNA is found structurally in the form of chromatin only during interphase; this changes at the end of the cell cycle when the cell is ready to replicate. At this point, the chromatin condenses, with the aid of proteins, into chromosomes. Chromosomes must be replicated, divided, and during meiosis be passed successfully to the resulting daughter cells. Chromosomes exist either as duplicated or unduplicated form. Unduplicated chromosomes are single linear strands, whereas duplicated chromosomes, which are copied during the S phase of interphase and contain two copies of the same chromosome which are joined at the centromere.

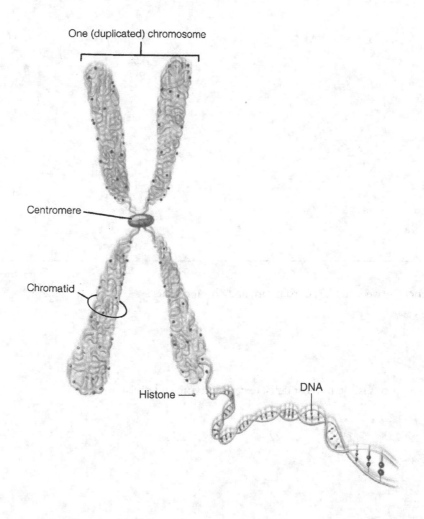

Figure 6.5

Mitosis.

Chromosome Extraction Procedure

1. Using a toothpick, gently scrape the inside of your cheek. Smear the scrapings onto the slide and add a drop of water, Make sure not to let the tissue dry out.
2. Carefully blot off only the excess water with the corner of a kim-wipe.

3.   Add 2–3 drops of 8% HCl acid to the tissue. Allow it to sit for three minutes. The HCl acid hydrolyzes the genetic material, opening the bonds between atoms, and allows the stain to better penetrate the chromosomes.
4.   VERY CAREFULLY blot the HCl acid off the slide as before.
5.   Add 2–3 drops of aceto-orcein stain to the tissue and allow to sit 4–5 minutes. DO NOT ALLOW THE STAIN TO DRY OUT. Add more stain if necessary.
6.   Blot excess stain off the slide, being careful to leave a small amount still on the tissue.
7.   Place the slide on a smooth flat surface. Add a cover slip. Place the slide into a fold of the paper towel. Press firmly down on the coverslip using the ball of the thumb.
8.   The acetic acid in the stain causes cytoplasm to gradually swell. The gentle pressure on the cover slip will therefore spread apart the chromosomes so that they can be studied. Your slide is now ready for examination under a compound microscope.
9.   Draw a representation of the chromosomes you observed under the microscope in the space provided below.

12. What is the difference between DNA, chromatin, and chromosomes?

13. Why are chromosomes not visible in most cells, except carrying cell division?

Meiosis & Mendelian Genetics

7

Objectives—Students will be able to:

- Explain the processes involved in Meiotic cell division
- Differentiate between the stages of Meiosis
- Differentiate between Mitosis and Meiosis
- Create a model of cellular division
- Explain the connection between Inheritance (Mendelian) Genetics and Meiosis
- Explain the laws of segregation and independent assortment
- Define the major terms associated with Inheritence Genetics
- Solve problems associated with monohybrid and dihybrid crosses
- Distinguish between incomplete dominance and codominance
- Explain the significance of lethal inheritance in genetics
- Identify all symbols associated with pedigrees
- Identify the mode of inheritance in pedigrees
- Identify the genotype and phenotype of individuals in a pedigree

INTRODUCTION

Meiosis includes a set of two successive cell divisions that serve to separate homologous chromosome pairs and thus reduce the total number of chromosomes by half. The meiotic process includes two sequential nuclear divisions that must occur prior to the formation of gametes (sperm and eggs). This process is referred to as a reduction division since the 4 daughter cells generated from the division of the diploid parental cell are haploid. The stages of Meiosis I are Prophase I, Metaphase I, Anaphase I and Telophase I (Figure 7.1) and of Meiosis II are Prophase II, Metaphase II, Anaphase II and Telophase II (Figure 7.1).

Meiotic Prophase I refers to the period after interphase, during which the homologous chromosomes pair, condense and recombine. Crossing over (Figure 7.2) is the recombination event that occurs during this stage. Recombination occurs at the chiasma (pl. chiasmata), the point where the chromosomes connect to swap a piece of the chromosome arm to result in a crossing over event. The defining sign indicating the end of Prophase I is the breakdown of the cell's nuclear envelope, and the extension of the meiotic spindle fibers forming closer associations with the paired chromosomes. The spindle fibers, composed of microtubules, with the aid of associated motor proteins, mediate chromosome movement during the stages of cellular division.

Metaphase I is the stage before the first division where pairs of interlocked homologous chromosomes line up in the middle of the cell. The spindle fibers attach onto the chromosomes at the kinetochore, which are located on the centromere. At this point the homologous chromosomes are attached to the spindles that have extended from the centrioles, forming the asters, at the opposite poles of the cell. In most meiotic systems, meiosis will not continue until all of the homologous pairs are properly oriented at the metaphase plate. Homologous chromosomes are oriented randomly at the plate, such that the paternally derived homolog may point toward one spindle pole, while in the adjacent set the maternally derived homologous chromosome is oriented toward the same pole.

Anaphase I refers to the stage where the homologous chromosomes segregate randomly and independently from each other moving to opposite poles of the cell. Telophase I is the stage where the endomembrane system reforms, which includes the nuclear envelope, Golgi apparatus and Endoplasmic Reticulum and the two haploid daughter cells are formed at the end of the cytokinesis event. There is a gap period between Meiosis I and Meiosis II, this period of time is termed, interkinesis. This is a shortened version of interphase where the synthesis of DNA does not occur.

Following interkinesis the cell will enter Meiosis II. Prophase II consists of the breaking of the nuclear envelope and the formation of the spindle fibers. The chromosomes align themselves on a new pair of spindles, with their sister chromatids oriented toward opposite poles, Metaphase II. Being that DNA replication did not occur during interkinesis each chromosome still consists of the two sister chromatids. There are no opportunities for pairing or recombination at this stage due to the prior separation of homologs at anaphase I.

The start of anaphase II is signaled by the separation of sister chromatids, and the movement of the two sister chromatids to opposite poles. At telophase II, the sisters have reached opposite poles and the nuclei begin to reform. The second cell division finishes at this time. Thus, at the end of the second meiotic division, there will be four haploid daughter cells, each with a single copy of each chromosome.

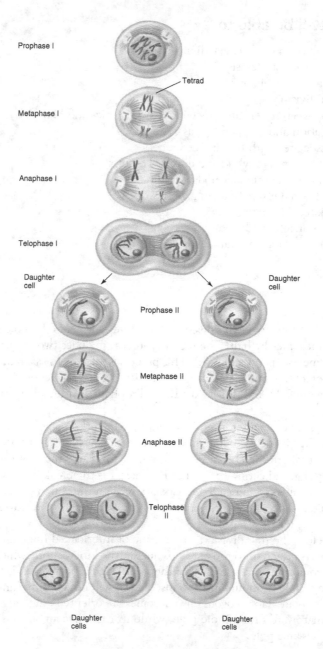

Figure 7.1

The stages in Meiosis.

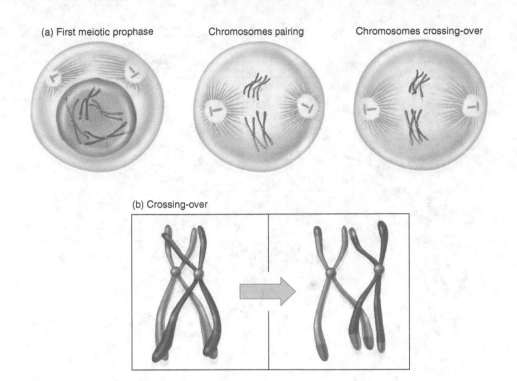

(a) First meiotic prophase   Chromosomes pairing   Chromosomes crossing-over

(b) Crossing-over

Figure 7.2
Crossing Over.

TASK 1—MEIOSIS AND GAMETOGENESIS

Gametes (sperm and eggs) are haploid reproductive cells that are the end result of the process of **gametogenesis**. In mammals and many other vertebrates, gametes and gametogenesis differ between males and females; males produce sperm through the process of **spermatogenesis** (Figure 7.3) while females produce eggs via **oogenesis** (Figure. 7.4). Both spermatogenesis and oogenesis are examples of Meiosis in action.

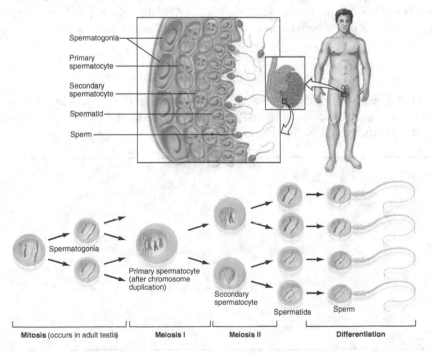

Spermatogonia
Primary spermatocyte
Secondary spermatocyte
Spermatid
Sperm

Spermatogonia
Primary spermatocyte (after chromosome duplication)
Secondary spermatocyte
Spermatids
Sperm

Mitosis (occurs in adult testis)   Meiosis I   Meiosis II   Differentiation

Figure 7.3
Spermatogenesis.

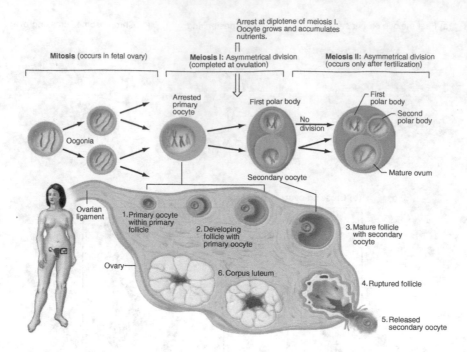

Figure 7.4

Oogenesis.

Sperm is produced in the **seminiferous tubules** of the **testes**. Within the seminiferous tubules, spermatogonia (parent cell) constantly replicate mitotically throughout the life cycle of males. Some of the **spermatogonia** move inward towards the lumen of the tubule to begin meiosis. At this point, they are called **primary spermatocytes**. Meiosis I of a primary spermatocyte produces two **secondary spermatocytes**, each with a haploid set of chromosomes. Meiosis II separates the sister chromatids of each chromosome and produces two haploid **spermatids** that mature and differentiate into **sperm** cells via **spermiogenesis**.

In females, **oogenesis** occurs in the ovaries. Unlike spermatogonia, oocytes are not produced continuously. **Oogonia**, which are produced during early fetal development, reproduce mitotically to produce **primary oocytes**. In humans, the ovaries of a newborn female contain all the primary oocytes that she will ever have. At birth, primary oocytes begin meiosis I, but are arrested in prophase I. At puberty, circulating hormones stimulate growth of the primary oocytes in the **follicles** (surrounding tissue) each month. Just before ovulation, the oocyte completes meiosis I producing a **Graafian follicle** which contains the haploid **secondary oocyte**. Meiosis II proceeds but is not completed until fertilization occurs.

Procedure

Examine the prepared slide of seminiferous tubules. Draw the image in the space below. Locate the spermatogonia, primary spermatocytes, secondary spermatocytes, spermatids and mature sperm and label each of these cells on your drawing. Next to each labeled term identify the ploidy number associated with each cell type.

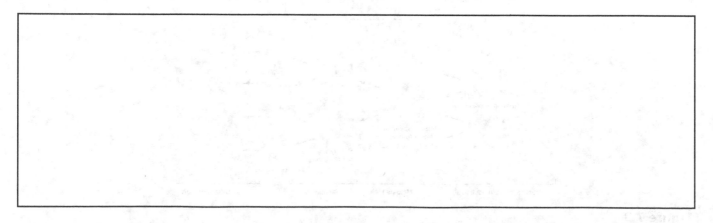

Examine a cross section of an ovary and draw what you see in the space provided below. Locate and label the developing follicle with the egg inside on your drawing.

```

```

Examine the two types of sperm smears available at your table. Draw what you see in the space provided below. Locate and identify any differences you may see between the two smears.

Questions
1. Why do gametes have only half the number of chromosomes as the original parent cell? Why is this important?

Examine the Lily Anther First Division and Lily Anther Second Division slides and draw what you see in the space provided below. Locate and identify any differences you may see between the two sections. Label any important structure. Label the stages of cellular division the cells are in.

```

```

Questions
1. Why do gametes have only half the number of chromosomes as the original parent cell? Why is this important?

2. Would evolution occur without the events of meiosis and sexual reproduction? Why or why not?

3. After which meiotic division in gametogenesis does the germ cell become haploid?

4. What differences are there between the meiotic divisions in a developing sperm and those in a developing ovum?

5. Why is meiosis referred to as reduction division?

6. If a species has 24 chromosomes in the nucleus prior to meiosis, what number will each cell have after meiosis is complete?

7. How do sperm and eggs differ in size? (**Hint**: consider size and the quantity of each gamete). Explain a possible reason for these differences.

8. What would happen if females produced 100's or 1000's of eggs during each cycle? What if males were born with a limited number of sperm?

Task 2—LET'S MAKE GAMETES! Simulate a diploid cell with 4 chromosomes going through Meiosis

1. Using the chromosome model kit, obtain 4 chromosomes. If any sister chromatids are attached separate them from one another. If there are any plastic buttons inserted into the chromosomes selected from the kit remove them from the model chromosomes. Note: The circle printout that you will be using throughout this exercise does not represent the entire cell it only represents the cell's nucleus.

2. Select two homologous, pre-Synthesis (pre-"S" phase) chromosome pairs. Make sure each homologous pair is exactly alike including the connectors.

9. Why would making sure that each homologous pair are exactly the same be important to this model?

3. Select a unique shaped sticker for each *pre-S* homologous pair. Make each a different color.

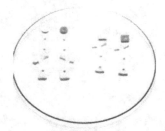

10. Why is it important for each plastic button to be a different color in this model?

4.   Now simulate what this nucleus would look like *AFTER* the *S phase*, but prior to entering the division stage. Put duplicated stickers in each sister chromatid.

> 11.   In your own words, what has happened between the previous step and this one? What has happened to the number of chromosomes?

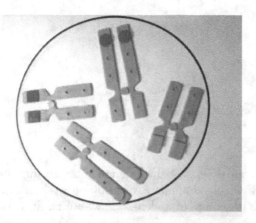

> 12.   What has happened to the amount of genetic material at this point of the cycle?

> 13.   What has happened to the number of chromosomes at this point of the cycle?

5.   Simulate this nucleus at metaphase of Meiosis I. *Please realize that even though we are still putting chromosomes inside of a circle, there actually is NO nuclear membrane post prophase.* This is very important—**is this the ONLY way the homologous chromosomes could have lined up? If so, simulate alternate alignments on the metaphase plate. Draw the alignment options in the space provided below; make sure to label any important structures.**

> 14.   How many different combinations can occur at this point of Meiosis I?

6. Simulate anaphase I and telophase I. What would be the resulting daughter cells at the end of Meiosis I from each of the alignments you simulated? Draw the results below. Make sure to label any important structures.

7. It is the chromosomal arrangements at the metaphase plate that will determine the different arrangements of resultant daughter cells. **Work in pairs**, divide the arrangements made in step 5 and simulate the resulting arrangements at the end of Meiosis I. At the end you should have four daughter cells per groups of students. Draw your results below. Label any important features.

15. Are there any duplicates?

16. Why do they exist?

17. Why is it alright to no longer consider them?

18.	Did the way square buttons separate affect the way circle buttons separate in any way? Why?

19.	This is an example of which Mendelian law?

8. Using the chromosome models at the end of Meiosis I and simulate the process of Meiosis II. In the space provided below draw all the possible combinations of resulting gametes.

Stop. Save your work and call for your instructor, be prepared to defend each step of this simulation.

Task 3—LET'S HAVE "UNPROTECTED SEX" WITH RANDOM PEOPLE!

If you call the square buttons set "A" and the circle buttons set "B", then you can call orange Big and pink small. For instance, if squares are "A" then an orange square would be considered big–A (Dominant allele), and pink would be little-a (recessive allele). Each of these letters (shapes) represents a gene. Each color would represent an alternate form of that gene, an allele.

20.	What is the term for an alternate state of a gene?

21.	How many genes are being dealt with in this simulation?

22.	How many alternate forms of a gene are being dealt with in this simulation?

23. What is the genotype of the original parent in this simulation?

24. What is the genotype of each of your gametes (disregarding duplicates)?

1. Each of you should now possess a unique gamete. This is your opportunity to practice "unsafe sex" with random people in the lab. Select anyone from another table and simulate fertilization using the chromosome models. Each individual will have "sex" twice using a DIFFERENT gamete during each fertilization event. Record the results of the mating in Table 7.1 below.

TABLE 7.1

GENOTYPE RESULTS

	Gamete 1 Genotype	Gamete 2 Genotype	Offspring Genotype
Student 1- Mating 1			
Student 1- Mating 2			
Student 2- Mating 1			
Student 2- Mating 2			
Student 3- Mating 1			
Student3- Mating 2			
Student 4- Mating 1			
Student 4- Mating 2			

25. What is the resulting genotype of the resulting offspring?

2. Design a table that would summarize the class data set. Use the data from each group's Table 7.1 to populate this table. Combine the phenotypic results together as a class on the board. Copy the results in the space below.

3. Observe and discuss the proportion of each genotype.

26. What Mendelian assortment ratio does this pattern seem to be approaching?

4. I hope you are now experiencing a light-bulb moment. At this moment you should realize the connection between meiosis, segregation, assortment, and inheritance genetics. If not, review this material repeatedly until the light bulb comes on. If you do this, you will have a grasp of this concept at a level such that you can never be confused again.

Task 4—WHY DON'T I LOOK EXACTLY LIKE MY SIBLINGS?

1. We are going to simulate crossing-over during prophase I using the chromosome models. Put the orange extensions on the ends of 2 of the 4 post-"S" homologous chromosomes (4 extensions total).

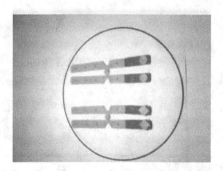

2. Consider prophase 1; place 2 plastic buttons in the sister chromatids of one homologue. Make the traits the same for the sister chromatids of an individual homologue.

27. What do the plastics buttons represent on the sister chromatids?

3. Do the same for the other homologue but use a different color.
4. Place a different shaped button onto the chromosome not undergoing crossing over.
5. Orient two sister chromatids from different homologues such that the arms with the alleles are touching.

6. Exchange the arms between two sister chromatids from <u>alternate homologues</u>.
7. Take the chromosome through the rest of Meiosis.
8. Draw the resulting model in the space provided below. Make sure to label all important features.

STOP Stop. Show the resulting chromosomes to your instructor before continuing.

> 28. Compare and contrast the gamete results from task 3 to that of task 4.

9. Now do the same thing on paper but instead of shapes, use letters. Compare the genotypes of the homologues before and after crossing-over.

> 29. What do the plastics buttons represent on the sister chromatids?

STOP Stop. Show your instructor before continuing.

Compare Mitosis and Meiosis in Table 7.2:

TABLE 7.2

MITOSIS VS. MEIOSIS

	Mitosis	Meiosis
Purpose of process		
Cell Types		
Number of cells generated per cycle		
Number of nuclear divisions per cycle		
Ploidy (n or 2 n) of daughter cells. (be specific)		
Daughter cells genetically identical to parent?		
Pairing of homologues		
Occurrence of crossing over		
What separates during anaphase? (be specific)		

Inheritance Genetics

Through his studies of the inheritance patterns of the garden pea, *Pisum sativum*, Gregor Mendel changed our understanding of heredity. Mendel studied characters that differed between plants and designed cross-fertilization experiments to understand how these characters are transmitted to the next generation. The results of Mendel's work refuted the prevailing hypothesis of blending inheritance and provided a new framework for understanding genetics. Ultimately, Mendel postulated two laws to explain heredity: (1) the **law of segregation** and (2) the **law of independent assortment**.

Monohybrid crosses and the law of segregation

The law of segregation states that during gamete formation (formation of egg and sperm) the alleles, alternate forms of a gene, on a pair of chromosomes segregate randomly so that each allele in the pair is received by a different gamete (daughter cell). For example, if you were to examine the gene responsible for petal color, you may discover that the gene can be expressed as either purple or white flowers. In this scenario, the gene is petal color, while the alleles are the colors purple and white. There is an equal probability that the allele for purple petal color will segregate into either daughter cell. There is also an equal probability that the white petal color will segregate into either daughter cell. Depending on which allele is expressed, petal color will vary. Examine Figure 7.5 below making sure that you can follow the path of each allele from parent to offspring.

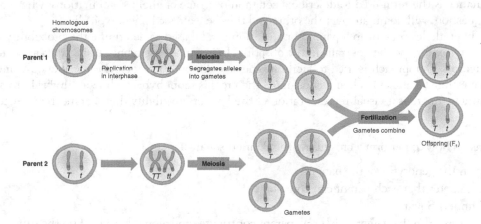

Figure 7.5
Schematic of Mendel's law of segregation.

In diploid organisms, all alleles exist in pairs; identical alleles within a pair are **homozygous**, while different alleles within a pair are considered **heterozygous**. Alleles are represented by a single letter that explains whether a particular trait is **dominant** or **recessive**. A dominant allele is determined to be dominant by observing the resulting phenotypes. When performing a cross between two true-breeding individuals, the trait in question has two versions of the phenotype. One of these versions of the phenotype is expressed at a time. The trait that is masked in the offspring is determined to be the recessive trait, while the trait that is expressed is the dominant trait. Dominant alleles are assigned an uppercase letter (A), while recessive alleles are lowercase (a). In general, a dominant trait is expressed when at least one of the alleles present in the resulting allelic pair is dominant (AA or Aa). In contrast, for a recessive trait to be expressed, both alleles within the pair must be recessive (aa). For example, when considering ear lobe shape, two phenotypes (attached and unattached) are apparent (Figure 7.6). This trait is regulated by a single gene where unattached ear lobes are dominant (A) while attached ear lobes (a) are recessive.

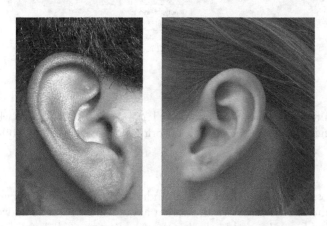

Figure 7.6
(a) Unattached (AA or Aa) vs. (b) attached earlobes (aa).

An organism's **genotype** (AA, Aa, aa) is the combination of alleles present whereas the **phenotype** is the physical expression of the genotype. In the earlobe shape example above, an individual can have a genotype of AA, Aa or aa. People with AA or Aa genotypes have the unattached earlobe phenotype (Figure 7.6a), while those with an aa genotype express the attached earlobe form (Figure 7.6b). Note that dominant traits can be either homozygous (AA) or heterozygous (Aa) while recessive traits are always homozygous (aa).

TASK 5—PATTERNS OF INHERITANCE I: Simple Dominance

Simple dominance is the term used to describe a common outcome of allelic combinations, where one allele, when a biallelic gene is in question, will dominate over the other and thus be expressed phenotypically.

Information about alleles present in a parental population can be used to determine the probability of different genotypic and phenotypic ratios for a variety of traits in the offspring. In instances when only 1 or 2 traits are being considered the **Punnett square** (Figure 7.7) approach is used to facilitate the calculations to predict the possible outcomes of the parental cross. When only one trait (2 alleles) is being considered the cross is **monohybrid** while a **dihybrid** cross involves 2 traits (4 alleles). The Punnett square is a visual representation of the laws of probability that dictate the predictable outcomes of parental crosses.

General instructions on how to perform a cross using the Punnett square approach:

1. Write down the genotypes of the parents
2. Note the gametes that each parent can contribute
3. Draw a Punnett Square
4. Across the top write the gametes that one parent contributes and along the side write the gametes contributed by the other parent
5. Perform the cross
6. Determine the genotypic and phenotypic ratios

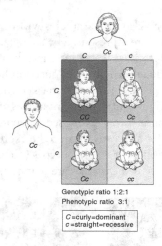

Genotypic ratio 1:2:1
Phenotypic ratio 3:1

C =curly=dominant
c =straight=recessive

Figure 7.7
Example of a Monohybrid cross.

In the example above (Figure 7.7), the genotypic ratio is 1:2:1 (1: CC, 2: Cc, 1: cc) while the phenotypic ratio is 3:1. Since C = curly hair and c = straight hair, ¾ of the possible offspring will have curly hair while only ¼ will have straight hair.

Procedure

You will now simulate a cross between two heterozygous individuals, Tt and Tt. Each group should obtain two pennies. You will flip the pennies simultaneously to represent the potential outcomes of a cross between two Tt individuals. A head represents the dominant tall allele (T) while a tail symbolizes the recessive dwarf allele (t). Before you begin flipping the pennies, perform the Tt x Tt cross in the Punnett square below to estimate the expected genotypic and phenotypic ratios.

Parent 1

Parent 2

Based on this cross, what do you anticipate the genotypic and phenotypic ratios to be? Write your predictions in Table 7.3.

TABLE 7.3

Expected Genotypic Ratio	
Expected Phenotypic Ratio	

1. Begin flipping the two pennies simultaneously for a total of 64 times. Record your results in Table 7.4.

TABLE 7.4

Response	Number
TT	
Tt	
tt	

Questions

30. What ratio of allele combinations did you observe?

31. What genotypes and phenotypes result from these crosses?

32. What are the genotypic and phenotypic ratios?

33. How did your results compare to your predictions?

34. Do you think your results would have been closer if you flipped the coins 6400 times instead of just 64? Why or why not?

35. Albinism, a recessively inherited trait, results in organisms that lack pigment in the skin, hair or eyes. A female with normal pigmentation, but who had an albino mother, mates with an albino male. They have one child. Using the information you have learned so far complete Table 7.5.

TABLE 7.5

Genotype of child's mother	
Genotype of child's father	
Possible gametes of mother	
Possible gametes of father	
Possible genotype and phenotype of the offspring	
Genotypic ratio of children	
Phenotypic ratio of children	

Dihybrid crosses and the law of independent assortment

Mendel's law of independent assortment states that alleles from different genes assort independently from one another during meiosis if they are located on separate chromosomes. For instance, alleles for the attached earlobe gene will assort independently from those that determine height as long as they are located on different chromosomes. The chance of getting any two events to happen at the same time is the product of the chance of each event independently happening at all. For example, the chance of getting allele "A" instead of allele "a " from gene 1, during gamete formation is 50%. However, the chance that that same gamete will receive both allele "A" from gene 1 AND allele "B" is the product of the probability of each event occurring independently from one another: 0.5 x 0.5 = 0.25 or 25% probability. Think of it like this - if you are flipping a coin and recording the results of each toss (heads or tails), and your friend is doing the same thing, do your tosses have any effect on the results of his? This is the question you will explore in the next procedure. No, because your two actions are not linked.

PROCEDURE

1. Use 2 pennies, 2 nickels
2. 1 penny and 1 nickel represent 2 pair of genes in a parent. The other penny and nickel represent the same pair of genes in the other parent.
3. Y = head on the penny (yellow), y = tail on the penny (white)
    R = head on the nickel (rough), r = tail on the nickel (smooth)
4. Both parents are heterozygous for both traits.
    YyRr x YyRr
5. Record the resulting offspring from a Punnett square under the expected probability on your data chart.
6. Toss all four coins (at the same time) 50 times and record results on your data chart.
7. Determine the percentage and record under experimental probability on your data chart below (Table 7.6).

TABLE 7.6

Phenotype	Expected	Observed Tally	Experimental
1st Dominant and 2nd Dominant			
1st Dominant and 2nd Recessive			
1st Recessive and 2nd Dominant			
1st Recessive and 2nd Recessive			

36. What ratio of allele combinations did you observe?

37. What genotypes and phenotypes result from these crosses?

38. What are the genotypic and phenotypic ratios?

39. How did your results compare to your predictions? Do you reject or fail to reject your null hypothesis. Explain.

40. Cross a homozygous dominate parent (DDWW) with a homozygous recessive parent (ddww)

   - Dominate allele for tall plants = D

   - Recessive allele for dwarf plants = d

   - Dominate allele for purple flowers = W

   - Recessive allele for white flowers = w

a. What is the probability of producing tall plants with purple flowers? Possible genotype(s)?

b. What is the probability of producing dwarf plants with white flowers? Possible genotype(s)?

c. What is the probability of producing tall plants with white flowers? Possible genotype(s)?

d. What is the probability of producing dwarf plants with purple flowers? Possible genotype(s)?

TASK 6—PATTERNS OF INHERITANCE II: Incomplete & Codominance

Inheritance of traits can occur in multiple forms. So far you have considered **complete dominance**, where a homozygous dominant or a heterozygous individual expresses the dominant phenotype, while an individual that is homozygous recessive expresses the recessive phenotype.

However, in certain cases a cross between two different allele forms results in a phenotypic expression that combines the two allelic traits. This type of inheritance is known as **incomplete dominance**. For example, if an offspring resulting from a cross between a red (RR) and a white (rr) snapdragon plant receives the dominant allele for red flower color (R) from one parent and the allele for white flower color (r) from the other, the resulting genotype will be Rr. The heterozygous form (Rr) of the plant will bear pink flowers since neither allele is completely dominant over the other (Figure 7.8).

Figure 7.8

Pink snapdragons are an example of incomplete dominance.

Expression of both alleles of a particular gene is known as **codominance**. When alleles are inherited codominantly, both phenotypes are expressed at the same time in the heterozygous condition in contrast to incomplete dominance where the heterozygote is an intermediate between the two homozygotes (Figure 7.9).

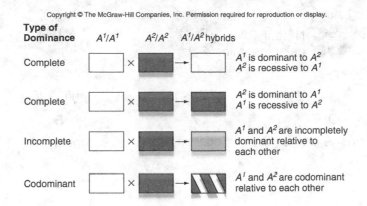

Figure 7.9

Different types of inheritance.

The ABO blood type system is an excellent example of codominance. Humans have four blood types, namely, **A, B, AB** and **O**. All individuals carry two alleles, one from each parent. In this system, both alleles inherited determine one's blood type, where a person with Type AB blood possesses phenotypic traits of both A and B blood types (Table 7.7).

TABLE 7.7	
RELATIONSHIP BETWEEN BLOOD TYPE AND GENOTYPE	
Blood type (phenotype)	Genotype
Type A	$I^A I^A$ or $I^A i$,
Type B	$I^B I^B$ or $I^B i$,
Type AB	$I^A I^B$
Type O	$i i$

For example, an individual with Type B blood can have two possible genotypes, $I^B I^B$ or $I^B i$, where I (dominant) and i (recessive) represent an allele from each parent (Table 7.7). The different blood types are characterized by the presence of a particular sugar molecule attached to the proteins on the surface of red blood cells (Figure 7.10). In Type A blood, the attached sugar molecule is galactosamine, while in Type B blood it is galactose. In contrast, individuals with Type O blood, have no sugars present on the surface of their red blood cells. These protein-sugar complexes are **antigens** that act as recognition markers for the immune system. The immune system is tolerant to its own antigens but produces **antibodies** against antigens that differ from its own. The antibodies formed bind to the antigens causing agglutination (clumping) and lysis of the foreign red blood cells. Therefore, an individual with Type A blood could not receive a blood transfusion from a Type B blood donor because the antigens on the donor's red blood cells will trigger an immune response from the recipient's antibodies. Thus, the Type A recipient will produce antibodies against the donor's Type B antigens.

When the wrong blood type is given to a patient, agglutination of the blood occurs and this can ultimately lead to death. Table 7.8 provides a quick overview of which blood types can donate to which, and which types can receive from which. A plus indicates that mixing of the donor and recipient blood types results in agglutination whereas a blank cell means that no agglutination occurs when the blood types are mixed.

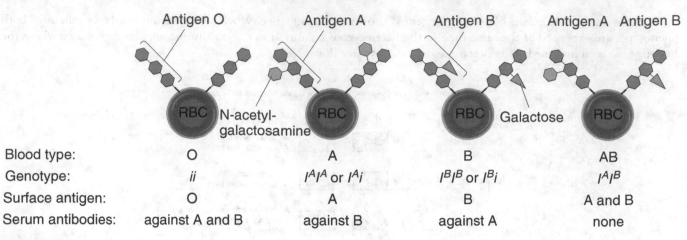

	Antigen O	Antigen A	Antigen B	Antigen A Antigen B
Blood type:	O	A	B	AB
Genotype:	ii	I^AI^A or I^Ai	I^BI^B or I^Bi	I^AI^B
Surface antigen:	O	A	B	A and B
Serum antibodies:	against A and B	against B	against A	none

Figure 7.10

Human ABO blood types.

TABLE 7.8

EFFECTS OF FIXING DIFFERENT BLOOD TYPES

	Recipient (Antibodies)			
Donor (Antigens)	A	B	AB	O
A		+		+
B	+			+
AB	+	+		+
O				

1. Determine the possible phenotypes of the F1 offspring when two pink snapdragons are crossed. Show your work in the space provided below.

Parent 1

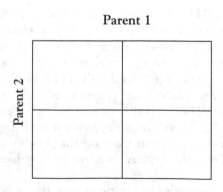

Parent 2

2. What would be the resulting genotypes of a cross between a pink and a white snapdragon? Show your work in the space provided below.

Parent 1

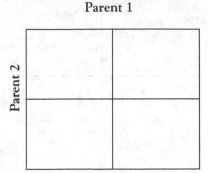

Questions

41. Why do you think that Type O is the universal donor and AB is the universal recipient?

42. There was a mix of up children in the maternity ward of a hospital. The children in question and their blood types are listed below.

Child 1: type A (genotype $I^A I^A$ or $I^A i$)

Child 2: type B (genotype $I^B I^B$ or $I^B i$)

Child 3: type AB (genotype $I^A I^B$)

Child 4: type O (genotype ii)

Which child or children could belong to a couple having AB and O blood types?

43. Based on the previous question, is it possible to prove paternity based on blood types? Explain.

44. A woman with Type O blood has a child with the same blood type. Can the child's father have Type AB blood? Why or why not?

Another trait involved in blood typing is the Rh factor (Table 7.9). The Rh factor works along the principle of simple dominance instead of codominance. An individual who is Rh positive possesses the Rh antigen on his/her blood cells, while someone who is Rh negative lacks Rh antigens on their blood cells. Generally, the Rh status of an individual is always included with the blood type. For example, a person that is B+ has Type B blood and is Rh positive. This information is important during pregnancy since Rh incompatibility can develop in women that are Rh- and have an Rh+ developing fetus. Mixing of maternal and fetal blood through the placenta can cause the mother to develop antibodies against the Rh antigens from the baby. This condition is usually not harmful to the first child but may cause mild to severe symptoms during subsequent pregnancies since the mother's Rh antibodies attack the Rh antigens of the developing fetus.

TABLE 7.9

RH FACTOR

Rh factor	Possible genotypes
Rh⁺	Rh⁺/Rh⁺ Rh⁺/Rh⁻
Rh⁻	Rh⁻/Rh⁻

Determining blood type

Procedure

1. Prepare your station by obtaining the following supplies:
   a. 5 small plastic blood typing trays
   b. Toothpicks for mixing
   c. Five bottles of blood (on your table) representing five different individuals
   d. One bottle representing A antibodies
   e. One bottle representing B antibodies
   f. One bottle representing Rh antibodies

2. You will use each blood typing tray to determine the blood type of a particular individual. Note that each tray contains 3 wells, labeled A, B and Rh.

3. Add 3 drops of blood from individual 1 to every well in a blood typing tray.

4. Add 3 drops from the bottle labeled A antibodies to the well labeled A.

5. Add 3 drops of B antibodies to the well labeled B.

6. Add 3 drops of Rh factor solution to the well labeled Rh.

7. Mix each well with a toothpick. **Note:** Use a different toothpick for each well and tray.

8. After 1 min, examine the tray for the presence of crystals. Presence of crystals, indicates agglutination and a positive test* for a particular blood type and Rh factor.

9. Repeat steps 3-8 for the remaining individuals.

*Important note: In this particular experiment, agglutination indicates a positive test for a particular blood type. For example, if agglutination occurs in well A, then the individual has blood type A. However, when working with real blood (i.e. for the purposes of transfusions), agglutination would be a negative result. With regular blood, agglutination would indicate that the antibodies of one's blood detected a foreign substance (an antigen), causing an immune response and cell lysis.

Record your results in Table 7.10. Note which wells agglutination occurs in each tray. Based on your results, determine the blood type of the five individuals examined.

TABLE 7.10

BLOOD TYPING

Individual	Agglutination (Yes or No)			
	Well A	Well B	Rh factor (+/–)	Blood type
1				
2				
3				
4				

TASK 9—ANALYZING PEDIGREES

A **pedigree** is a map of relatives that is used to determine the inheritance pattern of a particular disease or trait. This map usually includes the gender of each family member, how each is related (through lines connecting individuals) and also provides information about genetic traits. Certain symbols are used to indicate these variables (Figure 7.11).

Questions

45.   What would you look for in a pedigree to determine if a trait was dominant?

46.   What would you look for in a pedigree to determine if a trait was recessive?

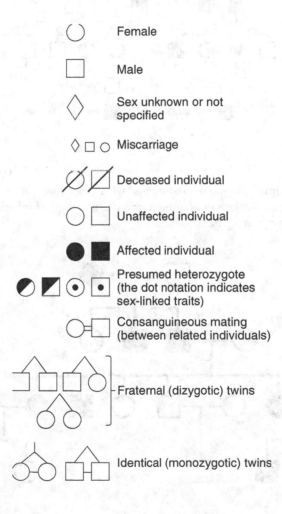

Figure 7.11
Symbols used in pedigree analysis.

47. The following is a pedigree for albinism. (a) Determine if the pedigree demonstrates a dominant or recessive mode of inheritance. Explain. (b) Assign genotypes for each individual for every generation.

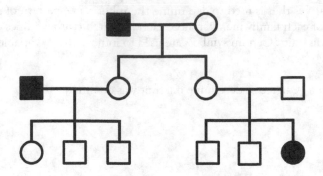

48. The following is a pedigree for Polydactyly. (a) Determine if the pedigree demonstrates a dominant or recessive mode of inheritance. Explain. (b) Assign genotypes for each individual for every generation.

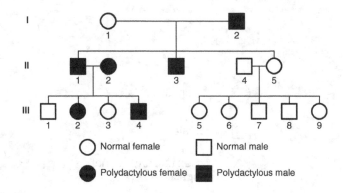

49. Below is a pedigree where multiple individuals are afflicted with Brachydactyly or shortening of the digits. (a) Determine if the pedigree demonstrates a dominant or recessive mode of inheritance. Explain. (b) Assign genotypes for each individual for every generation.

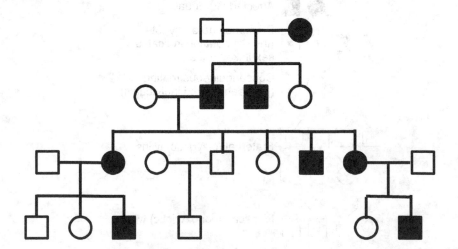

DNA & Its Interacting Molecules

8

Objectives

- Students will be able to differentiate between positive and negative controls.
- Students will be able to identify/design positive and negative controls when presented with experimental development scenarios.
- Students will be able to identify and determine the structure and function of the macromolecules and their subunits.
- Students will be able to use different reagents to identify the presence of macromolecules in known and unknown solutions.
- Students will be able to differentiate between positive and negative test for each of the macromolecules.
- Students will be able to compare and contrast the results of each test to identify differences in the intensity of the reactions.
- Students will be able to identify and explain whether a reaction is undergoing a dehydration synthesis or hydrolysis reaction.
- Students will be able to differentiate between an oxidation reaction and a reduction reaction.

BIO-MOLECULES

Biological organisms utilize four major classes of macromolecules in every biochemical reaction that occurs in the body of the organism: carbohydrates, proteins, lipids and nucleic acids. These organic compounds, carbon-based molecules, are important for proper cellular functioning and each plays a different role within the cell. Carbohydrates provide the primary source of energy or "fuel" for cells and are used to support cell walls of bacteria, fungi and plants. Proteins function as structural elements within the cell and aid in the transport of molecules across membranes. Proteins also regulate cellular activities (enzymes and hormones) and are important components of the immune system (antibodies). Lipids are not only used for "storage" of excess fuel but are an integral structural part of cell membranes. Finally, nucleic acids (DNA and RNA), the "information center" of the cell, comprise our genes, regulate cell function, and are involved in energy transfer. In addition, both DNA and RNA participate in cellular replication.

Many biological molecules are polymers comprised of smaller subunits (monomers) held together by covalent bonds. Carbohydrates, for example, are composed of varying combinations of monosaccharides (*e.g.* glucose, ribose, deoxyribose) that can be joined to form disaccharides (*e.g.* sucrose, maltose) and polysaccharides (*e.g.* starch, glycogen, cellulose, chitin). Similarly, proteins are made from unique combinations of amino acids. Monomers are linked together by dehydration synthesis (condensation) reactions in which a water molecule is removed, covalently bonding the two subunits (Figure 8.1a). Conversely, the bond between monomers can be broken by the addition of a water molecule, a process referred to as hydrolysis (Figure 8.1b).

Although all macromolecules are characterized by the presence of a carbon backbone, the four classes vary in their elemental structure and thus, their chemical properties (Figure 8.2). The functional groups impart different solubility and polarities to each type of macromolecule. For instance, lipids, which are made of fatty acids and have very little oxygen, are nonpolar and is soluble in water (hydrophobic). Proteins, on the other hand, are polymers of amino acids covalently linked by peptide bonds. Because amino acids are polar, non-polar, charged or aromatic, the properties of the resulting proteins vary in accordance with the type of amino acids that comprise them.

Throughout this lab, you will learn about the use of controls as standards for comparison and their role in identifying unknown solutions. Controls are an essential component of every experiment because they help eliminate alternate explanations of experimental results. In general, a control is defined as any variable that is kept constant throughout the entire experiment and is compared to the experimental sample(s) being tested. There are two types of controls: negative and positive. A negative control helps minimize false positives by providing a known negative result for a given experimental treatment. Thus, a negative control provides an example of what the results should look like if the experimental manipulation had no effect on the variable of interest. A positive control, on the other hand, helps minimize false negatives by demonstrating what a positive result should look like if the experimental manipulation produces a change. For example, when testing for the presence of salt in a substance, a salt solution would serve as the appropriate positive control and distilled water as the negative control. By applying your knowledge about basic macromolecule structure and using the proper controls you should be able to identify any unknown compound.

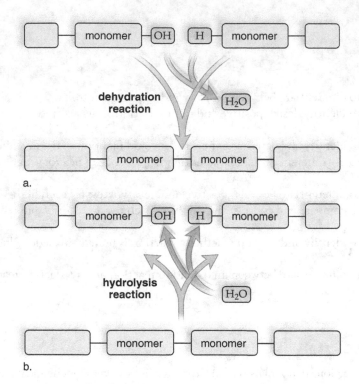

Figure 8.1

(a) Dehydration Synthesis reaction to build polymers (b) Hydrolysis reaction to break polymers apart into its subunits.

1. How do mono-, di- and polysaccharides differ in structure? Give examples of each.

2. How do mono-, di-, and polysaccharides differ in function?

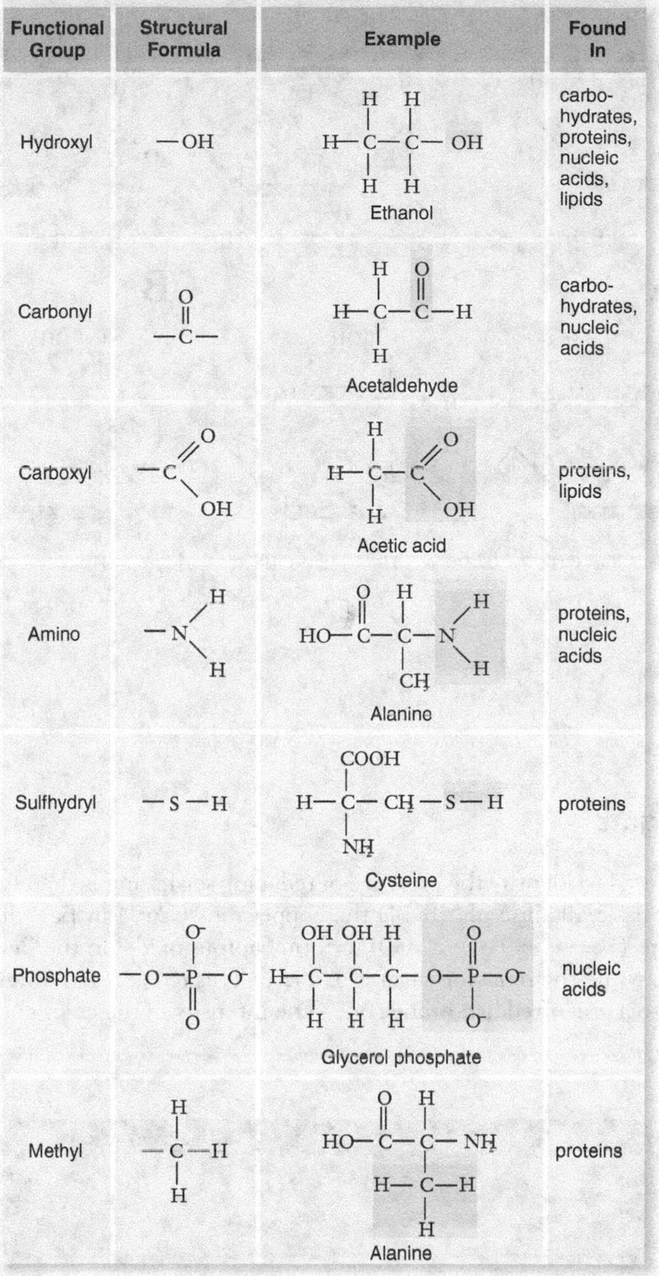

Functional Group	Structural Formula	Example	Found In
Hydroxyl	—OH	Ethanol	carbo-hydrates, proteins, nucleic acids, lipids
Carbonyl	O‖ —C—	Acetaldehyde	carbo-hydrates, nucleic acids
Carboxyl	—C⟨O‖OH	Acetic acid	proteins, lipids
Amino	—N⟨H H	Alanine	proteins, nucleic acids
Sulfhydryl	—S—H	Cysteine	proteins
Phosphate	—O—P—O⁻ (with O⁻ above and O below)	Glycerol phosphate	nucleic acids
Methyl	—C—H with H above and H below	Alanine	proteins

Figure 8.2
Major Functional Groups.

Task 1—CARBOHYDRATES

Carbohydrates are molecules made of simple sugars with Carbon (C), Hydrogen (H) and Oxygen (O) in a ratio of 1:2:1. **Monosaccharides** (Figure 8.3A) are made of single sugar molecules while **disaccharides** (Figure 8.3B) and **polysaccharides** (Figure 8.3C) are composed of two or more sugar molecules, respectively.

Monosaccharides contain either aldehyde (–CHO) or ketone (–C = O) side groups that reduce oxidizing compounds. A molecule is oxidized if it loses an electron or hydrogen atom and is reduced when it gains an electron or hydrogen atom. Collectively, the two processes are referred to as a **redox** reaction because when one molecule is oxidized, another is reduced.

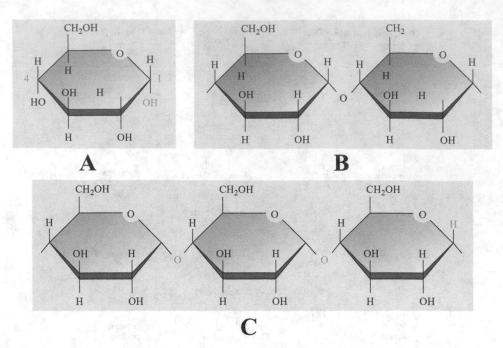

Figure 8.3
Carbohydrate Molecules.

I. Examine Reducing Sugars

Benedict's reagent can be used to identify the presence of reducing sugars and is therefore a good indicator for the presence of some carbohydrates. At basic/alkaline pH (8-14) the copper ions (Cu^{2+}) in Benedict's reagent are reduced by the monosaccharide functional groups (i.e. –CHO or –C = O) to form cuprous oxide. In the Benedict's test for reducing sugars, the Benedict's reagent is reduced while the reducing sugar is oxidized. This redox reaction results in a tractable color change going from a **light blue** solution to a **green/reddish orange** one. The intensity of the color change is indicative of the amount of reducing sugar present (Figure 8.4).

Figure 8.4
Bendict's Test samples (A) negative test (no reducing sugars present); (B) positive (small amount of reducing sugars present); (C) positive (larger amount of reducing sugars present); (D) positive (abundance of reducing sugars present).

Record your predictions and results in Table 8.1 below

TABLE 8.1
BENEDICT'S TEST & IODINE TEST

Tube	Solution	Benedict's Test Results		Iodine Test Results	
		Expected (color)	Observed (color)	Expected (color)	Observed (color)
1	10 drops onion juice				
2	10 drops potato juice				
3	10 drops sucrose				
4	10 drops 1.5% glucose				
5	10 drops 0.5% glucose				
6	10 drops 0.25% glucose				
7	10 drops distilled water				
8	10 drops reducing sugar				
9	10 drops starch				
10	10 drops unknown solution				

Procedure 8.1: Benedict's Test for Reducing Sugar

1. Obtain ten test tubes and number them 1–10.
2. Add the materials listed in Table 1 to each of your tubes.
3. Half fill a 500 mL beaker with water. Place it on the hot plate at your station and allow it to come to a gentle boil.
4. In the meantime, predict the color changes you expect to occur in each tube and record them in Table 8.1. Also mark which tube you think is the positive control with a* and which is the negative control with a**.
5. Add 2 mL of Benedict's reagent to each tube.
6. Place all 10 tubes in the gently boiling water bath for 3 minutes. Observe the tubes for any change in color during this time.
7. After 3 minutes, remove the tubes and allow them to cool to room temperature. Record the color of each tube in Table.

Benedict's Test for Reducing Sugars—Questions

3. In your own words, what is a negative control?

4. In your own words, what is a positive control?

5. Why are these types of controls (positive and negative) used in experiments?

6. What observations indicate a positive test for reducing sugars?

7. Using Table 8.1, identify the positive and negative controls for the Benedict's Test. Explain.

8. Is there a relationship between the amount of reducing sugars in the solution and the intensity of the reaction? Explain.

9. Will the Benedict's reagent detect the presence of ALL sugars? Explain.

10. Rank the solutions from non-reducing sugar to strongest reducing sugar.

11. Based upon the results of the Benedict's test what can you conclude about your unknown solution?

I. Examine Starch

Starch is a polysaccharide often used by organisms for storage of metabolic energy. Unlike the simpler mono- and disaccharides, starch is a structurally complex polymer (Figure 8.5). Iodine (iodine-potassium iodide, I_2KI) reacts with the

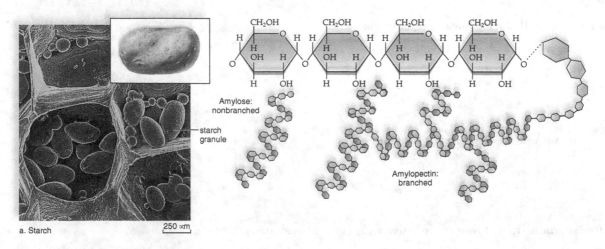

a. Starch

250 ᴧm

Figure 8.5
Starch a polysaccharide molecule used for storage in plants.

three-dimensional structure of this molecule, resulting in a color change (going from **yellow** to **blue-black**, Figure 8.6). In this exercise, we will test the substances previously examined for the presence of reducing sugars for starch.

Procedure 8.2: Iodine Test for Starch

1. Obtain ten test tubes and number them 1–10.
2. Add the materials listed in Table 8.1 to each of your tubes.
3. Predict the color changes you expect to occur in each tube and record them in Table 8.1. Also mark which tube you think is the positive control with a * and which is the negative control with a **.
4. Add 10 drops of iodine to each tube.
5. Record the color of each tube in Table.

Figure 8.6
Iodine Test Samples (A) Negative (no starch present); (B) Positive (starch present).

Iodine Test for Starch—Questions

12. What type of carbohydrate are you testing for when you use the Iodine Test? Is this type of carbohydrate a mono-, di-, or polysaccharide?

13. What observations indicate a positive test for starch?

14. Explain the results seen in the following solutions:
    a. Onion Juice

    b. Potato Juice

15. Is there a relationship between the amount of starch in the solution and the intensity of the reaction? Explain.

16. Using Table 8.1, identify the positive and negative controls for the Iodine Test. Explain.

17. Based upon the results of the Iodine Test what can you conclude about your unknown solution?

Task 2—PROTEINS

Proteins are composed of amino acids covalently linked by peptide bonds (Figure 8.7b). All amino acids contain an amino group (–NH₂), a carboxyl group (–COOH), and a variable side chain (R-group, Figure 8.7a) by which they are categorized. Peptide bonds (C–N) form when the amino group of one amino acid reacts with the carboxyl group of another. The Biuret reagent, regularly colored **blue**, is used to identify proteins. When the copper ions (Cu^{2+}) in the reagent interact with peptide bonds, a **violet** color is produced (Figure 8.8). In order for the interaction between Cu^{2+} and the peptide bonds to result in a color change, a minimum of 4–6 peptide bonds is required. In general, the longer the protein chain is, the greater the intensity of the reaction.

Procedure 8.3: Biuret Test for Proteins

1. Obtain 8 test tubes and number them 1–8.
2. Add the substances listed in Table 8.2 to each test tube.
3. Predict the color changes you expect to occur in each tube and record them in Table 8.2 in the "Expected Results (color)" column. Also mark which tube you think is the positive control with a * and which is the negative control with a **.
4. Add 2 mL of Biuret Reagent to each test tube.
5. Record the color of each tube in Table 8.2 in the "Observed Results (color)" column.

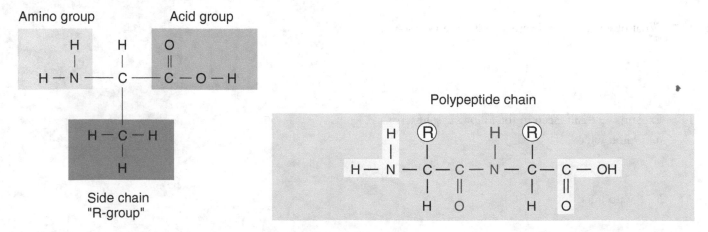

Figure 8.7

(a) Amino Acid Structure; (b) Protein composed of two amino acids and linked by a peptide bond (red).

Figure 8.8
Biuret Test Samples (a) negative (no protein present); (b) positive (protein present).

	TABLE 8.2		
	BIURET TEST		
Tube	Solution	Expected Results (color)	Observed Results (color)
1	2 mL egg albumen		
2	2 mL honey		
3	2 mL amino acid solution		
4	2 mL distilled water		
5	2 mL 0.5% protein solution		
6	2 mL 1% protein solution		
7	2 mL 3% protein solution		
8	2 mL unknown solution		

Biuret Test for Proteins—Questions

18.   What monomer comprises a polypeptide?

19.   In the Biuret Test, what molecular structure produces the reaction seen in the test?

20.   What observations indicate a positive test for proteins?

21. Using Table 8.2, identify the positive and negative controls for the Biuret Test. Explain.

22. Is there a relationship between the amount of proteins in the solution and the intensity of the reaction? Explain.

23. Compare and contrast the results seen in test tubes 3 & 5 of the Biuret Test.

24. Compare and contrast the results seen in test tubes 5, 6 & 7 of the Biuret Test.

25. Based upon the results of the Biuret Test what can you conclude about your unknown solution?

Task 3—LIPIDS

Lipids, which include triglycerides (fats), steroids, waxes, and oils, vary in function. While triglycerides and oils serve as energy-storage molecules, phospholipids aggregate to form cellular membranes which are important source of cholesterol, a necessary component of steroid hormones. All lipids share one characteristic; they are insoluble in water (hydrophobic) because they have a high proportion of non-polar carbon-hydrogen bonds and can only dissolve in non-polar solvents such as ether, ethanol and acetone. This property can be used to test unknown solutions for the presence of lipids. One indicator commonly used is Sudan IV, a fat-soluble dye that binds to lipids when added to a solution (Figure 8.9).

Procedure 8.4: Solubility Test for Lipids

1. Obtain five test tubes and number them 1–5.
2. In this exercise, you will assess the solubility of lipids in polar and non-polar solvents. Predict what you expect to occur in each tube and record your predictions in Table 3 in the "Expected Results" column.
3. Add 1mL of vegetable oil to each tube followed by the solutions listed in Table 8.3.
4. Record your observations in Table 3 in the "Observed Results" column.

TABLE 8.3

SOLUBILITY TEST

Tube	Solution	Expected Results	Observed Results
1	3 mL water		
2	3 mL acetone		
3	3 mL honey		
4	3 mL 1% protein solution		
5	3 mL unknown solution		

8–10

Lipid Solubility—Questions

5.   Do lipids dissolve in water? Why or why not?

6.   Compare and contrast the results in test tube 1 & 2 of the Solubility Test.

7.   What did the solubility test demonstrate about the structure and solubility properties of a lipid?

8.   Based upon the results of the Solubility Test what can you conclude about your unknown solution?

Procedure 8.5: Sudan IV Test for Lipids

1.   Obtain six test tubes and label them 1–6.
2.   Add the substances listed in Table 8.4 to each test tube.
3.   Predict the color changes you expect to occur in each tube and record them in Table 8.4 in the "Expected Result (color)" column. Also mark which tube you think is the positive control with a* and which is the negative control with a**.
4.   Add 10 drops of water to and 2 mL of the Sudan IV reagent to each of the test tubes.
5.   Carefully cover each tube with parafilm and invert the tubes 2–3 times to mix the contents.
6.   Record the color of each tube in Table 8.4 in the "Observed Results (color)" column.

Figure 8.9
A stain known as Sudan IV combines with lipid molecules to produce a bright red color. This is an example of a positive result of the Sudan IV test (left). In a negative test using Sudan IV the stain does not combine with the lipid and will instead diffuse the red color throughout the solution (right).

TABLE 8.4

SUDAN IV TEST

Tube	Solution	Expected Results (color)	Observed Results (color)
1	1 mL salad oil		
2	1 mL honey		
3	1 mL distilled water		
4	1 mL 1% protein		
5	1 mL known lipid		
6	0.5 mL known lipid + 0.5 mL water		
7	1 mL unknown solution		

Sudan IV Test for Lipids—Questions

7. What observations indicate a positive test for lipids?

8. Using Table 8.4, identify the positive and negative controls for the Sudan IV Test. Explain.

9. Is there a relationship between the amount of lipids in the solution and the intensity of the reaction? Explain.

10. Based upon the results of the Sudan IV Test what can you conclude about your unknown solution?

Task 4—DISCHE DIPHENYLAMINE REAGENT TEST—NUCLEIC ACIDS

DNA and RNA are nucleic acids made of nucleotide subunits. One major difference between DNA and RNA is their sugar: DNA contains deoxyribose, whereas RNA contains ribose. DNA can be identified chemically with the Dische Diphenylamine test. Acidic conditions convert deoxyribose to a molecule that binds with diphenylamine to form a blue complex. The intensity of the blue color is proportional to the concentration of the nucleic acid.

Danger! Handle the Dische diphenylamine reagent carefully; it is toxic. Use gloves when handling the reagent and keep the stock solution under the hood.

Procedure: The Dische Diphenylamine Test for DNA

1. Half fill a 250mL beaker with water. Place it on a hot plate at your station and allow it to come to a gentle boil.
2. Obtain six test tubes and number them 1–6.

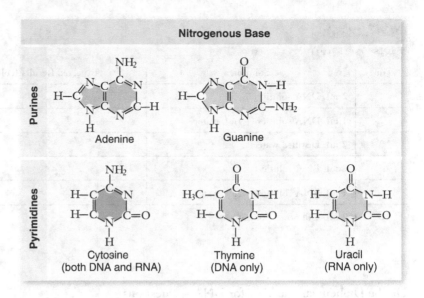

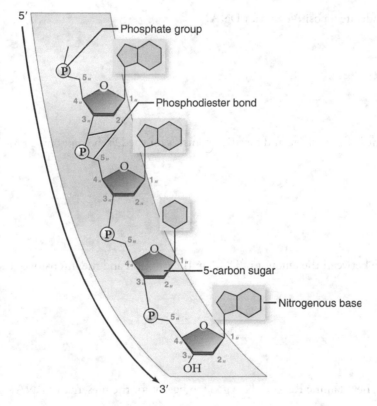

Figure 8.10

Basic nucleic acid structure.

3. Add the materials listed in Table 8.5.

4. Add 2 mL of the Dische diphenylamine reagent to each tube and mix thoroughly.

5. Place the tubes in a boiling water-bath for 10 minutes.

6. In the meantime, predict the color changes you expect to occur in each test tube and record them in Table 8.5. Also mark which tube you think is the positive control with an* and which is the negative control with a**.

7. After 10 minutes, transfer the tubes to an ice bath. Gently mix and observe the color of their contents as the tubes cool. Record your observations in Table 8.5.

*Dispose of all solutions in the Dische waste container in the hood.

TABLE 8.5

DISCHE DIPHENYLAMINE TEST

Tube	Solution	Expected Results (color)	Observed Results (color)
1	2 mL DNA solution		
2	1 mL DNA solution + 1mL water		
3	2 mL Distilled water		
4	2 mL RNA solution		
5	1 mL RNA solution + 1mL water		
6	2 mL Unknown Solution		

Dische Diphenylamine Test for DNA—Questions

11. What observations indicate a positive test for DNA?

12. Using Table 2.5, identify the positive and negative controls for the Dische diphenylamine Test. Explain.

13. Is there a relationship between the amount of DNA in the solution and the intensity of the reaction? Explain.

14. Would the Dische diphenylamine Reagent be a good indicator for the presence of RNA? Explain.

15. Based upon the results of the Dische Diphenylamine Test what can you conclude about your unknown solution?

Gene Expression

9

Learning Objectives

- Enable students to observe the experimental process called bacterial transformation,
- Demonstrate the relationship between the genetic constitution of an organism and its physical attributes,
- Enable students to observe the change in phenotype caused by the uptake and expression of a known plasmid sequence, and
- Reinforce the need for sterile technique when working with bacteria.

INTRODUCTION

The blueprint of life itself is found in DNA. But, life without its supporting molecules is not possible. DNA is transcribed into RNA. As RNA the blueprint that was in the DNA can now be read by the translational machinery to convert this blueprint message into proteins, the language of the cell. It is the proteins expressed in a cell that determines the physical and biochemical structural properties and function of a cell. It is the molecular machinery that transfers the information from DNA to RNA to a protein capable of performing a function within the cell that is essential to all life. This involves several complex pathways each of which is subject to regulation. The first step of this cellular pathway is the synthesis of an RNA molecule from the DNA template. This process is termed transcription. Upon exiting the nucleus, a mature RNA can be translated into a polypeptide sequence. This process is known as translation. These pathways happen, with some modification, in both eukaryotes and prokaryotes. As much as this process is regulated by the cell it can also be manipulated by researchers in biology, particularly in prokaryotes.

When we talk about DNA what is typically referred to is nuclear DNA, but there are other forms in which DNA is found, like plasmids. Plasmids are small, circular DNA molecules that exist apart from the chromosome(s) in most bacterial species, in the nucleoid region. Plasmids are not essential for survival of the host bacteria, in most cases. However, when bacteria are placed into certain environments, plasmids could give them that extra advantage that allows bacteria to survive and reproduce in these environments. Plasmids can carry genes that, when expressed, help bacteria survive. For instance, some plasmids can have genes that grant bacteria resistance to certain antibiotics. A bacterial cell containing such a plasmid can live and multiply in the presence of the antibiotic drug. Antibiotic-resistant bacteria like *Escherichia coli (E. coli)* isolated in many parts of the world contain plasmids that carry the genetic information for protein products that interfere with the action of many different antibiotics. In this laboratory, you will introduce a plasmid that contains an ampicillin-resistance gene into *E. coli*.

Biotechnology is the technological application of biological systems or their derivatives to make/modify products or processes for a specific use. Biotechnology plays a vital role in health care to manufacture hormones (*i.e.* insulin), antibiotics and vaccines, in agriculture to produce disease resistant crops, and in environmental preservation to make biodegradable products. Today, the most commonly used form of biotechnology is genetic engineering. This field involves the direct manipulation of genes, through the movement of DNA from one organism to another or from one species to another, to impart a particular characteristic, such as, pesticide/herbicide resistance, a longer shelf life, and increased nutritional value of agricultural crops to an organism of interest. Genetic engineering includes techniques such as transformation and cloning. While the latter process creates multiple copies of a desired gene, transformation, discovered by Frederick Griffith, alters the genetic code of a cell through the uptake, incorporation and expression of a foreign gene provided by a "donor" cell.

In order for transformation to be successful, three conditions are required: 1) a host into which the foreign DNA can be inserted, 2) a means of delivering the DNA into the host cells, and 3) a way to identify and select for the transformed cells. You will use the bacterium *Escherichia coli* as the host organism for the current experiment. *E. coli* are gram-negative bacteria that form the normal flora of the gut. In the digestive system, *E. coli* benefit their host by producing vitamin K as well as preventing other pathogenic bacteria from establishing residence. However, certain strains of *E. coli* are pathogenic and result in food poisoning, gastrointestinal and urinary tract infections, neonatal meningitis and pneumonia. *E. coli* is used extensively in biotechnology because it has only one chromosome composed of 5 million base pairs (less than 0.2% of the human genome), a short reproduction time (cell division every 20 minutes) and a fairly rapid growth rate.

Delivery of foreign DNA into the host cell is mediated by a vector. Commonly used vectors in genetic engineering include viruses and plasmids. In today's experiment you will use a plasmid to transport the gene of interest into the host *E. coli* cells. Because the chances of a successful transformation are small, an experimental setup that will allow researchers to identify transformed cells is crucial. One way to separate the transformed from non-transformed cells is by "tagging" the plasmid with a selectable marker. This is done by adding a gene to the plasmid that confers some type of selective advantage like antibiotic resistance to the host cells. For example, a plasmid containing a gene for ampicillin resistance (*pAMP*) can be used to transform the *E. coli* bacterium into an ampicillin resistant strain. Through the acquisition of this gene, *E. coli* will become resistant to ampicillin (an antibiotic similar to penicillin capable of killing the bacteria) enabling the bacterial cells to grow in its presence.

One plasmid that you will use is called *pUC18*. Plasmid *pUC18* contains only 2,686 nucleotide pairs (molecular weight = 2×10^6). The small size of this plasmid makes it less susceptible to physical damage during handling. In addition, smaller plasmids generally replicate more efficiently in bacteria and produce larger numbers of plasmids per cell. Plasmid *pUC18* contains an ampicillin-resistance gene that enables *E. coli* to grow in the presence of the antibiotic. Bacteria lacking this plasmid, or bacteria that lose the plasmid, will not grow in the presence of ampicillin. The ampicillin-resistance gene codes for the enzyme beta-lactamase (penicillinase), which inactivates ampicillin and other antibiotics in the beta-lactam family of antibiotics. The *lux* operon is found in the luminescent bacterium *Vibrio fischeri* and contains two genes that code for luciferase (the enzyme that catalyzes the light-emitting reaction) and several genes that code for enzymes that produce the luciferins (the substrates for the light-emitting reaction). The second plasmid's, the *lux* plasmid, MW is approximately 4.5×10^6.

In the laboratory, plasmids can be introduced into living bacterial cells by a process known as transformation. When bacteria are placed in a solution of calcium chloride ($CaCl_2$), they acquire the ability to take in plasmid DNA molecules. It increases the cell competency, the cell's ability to pick up a plasmid. This procedure provides a means for preparing large amounts of specific plasmid DNA, since one transformed cell gives rise to clones that contain exact replicas of the parent plasmid DNA molecule. Following growth of the bacteria in the presence of the antibiotic, the plasmid DNA can be readily isolated from the bacterial culture.

GENERAL PROCEDURE SUMMARY

In this exercise, plasmid *lux* and a control plasmid (*pUC18*) will be introduced into *E. coli* by transformation. There are four basic steps to the procedure:

Treat bacterial cells with $CaCl_2$ solution in order to enhance the uptake of plasmid DNA. Such $CaCl_2$-treated cells are said to be "competent." (This step should be performed by the instructor before or during the laboratory session.) Incubate the competent cells with plasmid DNA. Select those cells that have taken up the plasmid DNA by growth on an ampicillin-containing medium. Examine the cultures in the dark.

PROCEDURE

A. Preparation of competent cells (These steps were performed by the instructor)

1. Place a vial of $CaCl_2$ solution and the tube of *E. coli* in the ice bath.
2. Using a sterile pipet, transfer 590 µL $CaCl_2$ solution to the tube containing 50 µL of the bacteria.
3. Tap the tube with the tip of your index finger to mix the solution.
4. Incubate the cells for at least 10 minutes on ice. The cells are then called competent because they can take up DNA from the medium. If desired, the cells can be stored in the $CaCl_2$ solution for 12–24 hours.

Note: There are 2 plasmids involved in this experiment each group will only use 1 of the 2 plasmids. The instructor will assign which plasmid your group will use.

1. Label one small Eppendorf tube "C" (for control plasmid DNA) or one tube "lux" (for plasmid *lux* DNA)

2. Place both tubes in an ice bath.

3. Using a sterile micropipette, add 5 μL control plasmid to the tube labeled "C" or 5 μL plasmid *lux* to the tube labeled "lux". Make sure to keep all tubes in the ice until instructed otherwise (concentration = 0.005 μg/μL).

4. Gently tap the tube of competent cells with the tip of your index finger to ensure that the cells are in suspension.

5. Using a sterile transfer pipet, add 70 μL of the competent cells to each of the two tubes.

6. Tap each of these tubes with the tip of your index finger to mix these solutions, and store both tubes on ice for 15 minutes. During this time, one member of the group should obtain one additional tube. Add 35 μL of competent cells to each tube and label the tubes "NP" (no plasmid). Every group will have a no plasmid tube assigned to them.

7. HEAT SHOCK: Transfer all the tubes to a water bath preheated to 37°C, and allow them to sit in the bath for 5 minutes. Make sure you are able to identify which tubes below to your group before you place them in the water bath.

8. Use a sterile pipet to add 275 μL nutrient broth to the control and lux tubes and 150 μL of nutrient broth into the no plasmid tube.

9. Incubate the tubes at 37°C for 45 minutes. Use this time to make your prediction (Table 9.1) and answer questions.

C. Selection of cells that have taken up the plasmid by growth on an ampicillin containing medium

Note: There are a total of 6 plates per trial. Each group will be working with 3 plates. The instructor will assign the plates your group will work with.

1. Each group will obtain 3 agar plates from the instructor. Label the plates as indicated in Figure 9.1. Keep in mind the instructor assigned your group the treatments you will be working with.

2. Using a sterile pipet, remove 130 μL mixed bacterial suspension from the "C" tube, remove the lid from the "Control" plate, and dispense the bacteria onto the agar. Use a cell spreader to spread the bacteria evenly onto the agar surface.

   -Use of the cell spreader:

   a. Dip the cell spreader in ethanol. Pass the spreader across the flame of the ethanol lamp. Make sure you only pass it through the flame and not keep it in the flame. Once the ethanol has burned off keep the spreader still for about 30 seconds. This allows the spreader to cool down before you start spreading the cells. Once the spreader has cooled use the spreader to evenly distribute the cell suspension over the entire surface of the plate. Return the cell spreader to the ethanol contained <u>without flaming</u> and repeat the same procedure until you have plated al the bacteria.

3. Transfer 130 μL bacterial suspension from the "lux" tube to the "lux" plate and spread these cells onto the agar surface as described in the previous step.

4. Cells from the tubes that did not contain plasmids (NP) should be plated onto two plates (NP) as described in steps 2–3.

5. Replace the lids on the plates, and leave the plates at room temperature until the liquid has been absorbed (about 10 minutes).

6. Invert the plates and incubate them at 37°C.

D. Examine cultures in the dark

1. Retrieve your group's plates from the refrigerator.

2. Open each plate, one by one, to determine if *E. coli* growth occurred. If growth occurred, note the growth type (lawn or colonial). Record your results in Table 9. 2.

3. Allow at least 3 minutes for the eyes to adjust to the dark in a light-free room. View your plates and the plates of your classmates in the dark and then in the light. Record your results in the following table. Were the results as expected? Explain possible reasons for variations from expected results (Table 9.2).

4. Calculate Transformation Efficiency and answer questions.

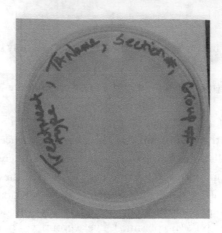

Figure 9.1
Petri Dish Label.

DATA ANALYSIS

State your scientific, null and alternative hypotheses regarding what you expect to see if the bacteria plated on the ampicillin rich medium were successfully transformed.

Scientific:

H_o:

H_a:

TABLE 9.1

PREDICTIONS			
Treatment	Expected Result (Growth or No Growth)	Bioluminescence (yes or no)	Reason For Expectations
LB^c			
LB/Amp^c			
LB^{NP}			
LB/Amp^{NP}			
LB/Amp^{lux}			
LB^{lux}			

9–4

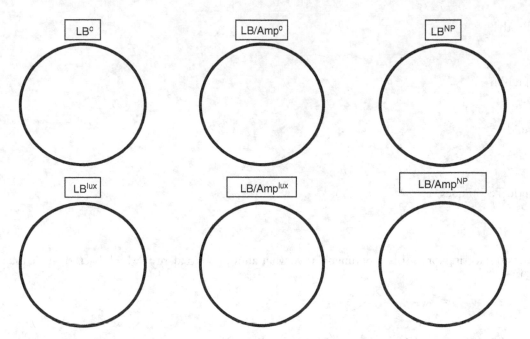

Figure 9.2

Experimental Predictions.

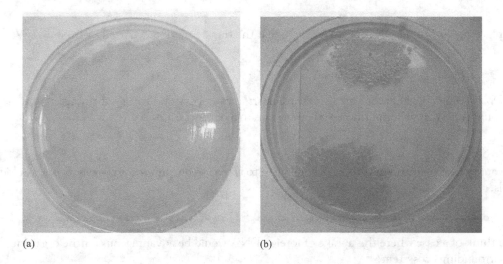

(a)   (b)

Figure 9.3

(a) Lawn Growth, (b) Colonial Growth.

Note: The colonial growth exhibited in this figure is seen in two large patches. Each patch holds hundreds of individual colonies.

Questions

1. What role did the following compounds or steps play in bacterial transformation?

    a. Calcium Chloride

    b. Heat Shock

    c. Agar

d. LB Broth

e. Ampicillin

f. Plasmid

g. Aseptic Techniques

2. What are you selecting for in this experiment? (*i.e.*, what allows you to identify which bacteria have taken up the plasmid?)

3. What does the phenotype of the transformed colonies tell you?

4. What one plate would you first inspect to conclude that the transformation occurred successfully? Why?

5. In nature, DNA uptake by different organisms can impart advantages as well as disadvantages to the host organism.
   a. When would genetic transformation be advantageous to a host organism?

   b. When would genetic transformation be maladaptive to a host organism? What consequences would there be for the host cells?

   c. Can you think of a case where the uptake of foreign DNA would be advantageous for the organism, but disruptive for the surrounding ecosystem?

TABLE 9.2

RESULTS

Treatment	Observed Growth Type	Bioluminescence (yes or no)	Reasoning for observed results
LB^c			
LB/Amp^c			
LB^{NP}			
LB/Amp^{NP}			
LB/Amp^{lux}			
LB^{lux}			

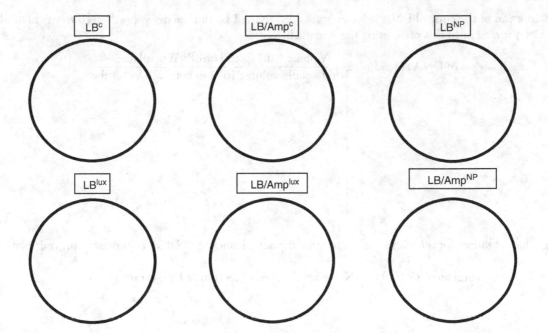

Transformation Efficiency: (Use the left side of the division to calculate the first transformation efficiency for the LB/Amp^c and use the right for the second set of calculation for the LB/Amp^{lux}).

Transformation efficiency calculations result in very large numbers. It is normally written in scientific notation. For example, if the calculated transformation efficiency is 1000 bacteria/µg of DNA it should be reported as 1×10^3 transformants/µg. Suppose that an efficiency is calculated as 5000 bacteria/µg of DNA. This would be reported as 5×10^3 transformants/µg.

6.   The total amount (µg) of plasmid DNA used can be calculated with the following formula.

$$\text{µg DNA} = \text{concentration (µg/µL) of DNA} \times \text{volume of DNA (µL)}$$

7.   Calculate the total volume of cell suspension prepared in the control DNA tube.

$$\text{Total volume (µL)} = \text{amount (µL) of plasmid} + \text{amount (µL) of LB} + \text{amount (µL) of cell suspension}$$

8. Since only a portion of the control DNA solution was added to the LB/Amp^c plate, you will need to calculate the fraction of DNA spread onto this plate using the formula below:

$$\text{Fraction of DNA spread} = \frac{\text{Volume (}\mu\text{L) spread on LB/Amp}^c\text{ plate}}{\text{Total sample volume (}\mu\text{L) in control DNA tube}}$$

9. Using the values obtained for questions 3–5, determine the actual amount of DNA (μg) present on your plate

$$\text{Total amount (}\mu\text{g) of DNA} = \mu\text{g of DNA} \times \text{Fraction of DNA spread}$$

10. Calculate transformation efficiency

$$\textit{Transformation Efficiency} = \frac{\textit{Total number of colonies on the LB/Amp}^C\textit{ plate}}{\textit{Total amount of DNA spread on LB/Amp}^C\textit{ plate}}$$

11. Repeat questions 3–10 to calculate the transformation efficiency for the LB/Amp^{lux} plate

12. Compare and contrast the number of colonies on each of the following pairs of plates. What does each pair of results tell you about the experiment?

a. LB^C and LB^{NP}

b. LB/Amp^{NP} and LB^C

c. LB/Amp^C and LB/Amp^{NP}

d. LB/Amp^C and LB^C

e. LB/Amp^{lux} and LB^{NP}

f. LB/Amp^{lux} and LB/Amp^{NP}

g. LB/Amp^C and LB/Amp^{lux}

h. LB/Amp^{lux} and LB^C

13. Do your results agree with your predictions in Table 9.1? Explain.

14. What factors could have affected transformation efficiency?

15. What transformation efficiency would you expect for all the other treatments?

16. Why do the cells transformed with *pUC18* and plasmid *lux* grow in the presence of ampicillin?

17. Name one enzyme that is produced by cells transformed with plasmid lux that is not produced by the cells transformed by *pUC18*.

18. Remembering that plasmid size will affect the efficiency of transformation, which plate would be expected to show the fewest colonies?

19. How would you improve or extend this experiment?

10

Molecular Biology—Crime Scene Investigation

Objectives

- Understand the chemical and structural differences between DNA and RNA.
- Become familiar with the process of DNA isolation.
- Perform a test to detect the presence of DNA.
- Learn how to separate molecules by gel electrophoresis.
- Perform selected techniques used in the field of forensic science.

Note

The tasks will be performed at different stations in the lab. Your group must all work on one station at a time. Your group will analyze one aspect of the crime scene at each station. The evidence collected from the crime scene will be provided by your instructor. Your instructor collected the evidence from the crime scene and it is up to your group to determine, according to the evidence, what occurred at the crime scene. You will need to provide a full story to your instructor by the end of class.

INTRODUCTION

Molecular biology uses cellular chemistry and genetics to study molecules critical to life. Employing techniques such as DNA isolation, Polymerase Chain Reaction (PCR) and gel electrophoresis, scientists can access nucleic acids (i.e. DNA and RNA) to examine and/or manipulate them. These techniques are utilized in a vast array of theoretical and practical applications such as medicine and forensic science, where they are used to solve crimes.

Nucleic acids are an important class of macromolecules because they comprise our genes, regulate cell function, and are a major component in cellular replication. Structurally, both DNA and RNA are long polymers composed of nucleotide subunits that are connected end to end by a **phosophodiester bond**. Each nucleotide consists of a phosphate group, a pentose sugar (deoxyribose in DNA vs. ribose in RNA) and a nitrogenous base (Fig. 10.1). In general, the nitrogenous bases are classified into one of two categories, **pyrimidines** (single ring structure) or **purines** (double-ring structure) as illustrated in Figure 10.1. In DNA, the nitrogenous bases present are Cytosine (C), Thymine (T), Adenine (A) and Guanine (G), while in RNA Thymine is replaced by Uracil (U). In addition to differences in base and sugar composition, DNA molecules are composed of two antiparallel strands (one runs 5'–3' and the other runs in the opposite direction, 3'–5') that are bonded together at the bases (A–T and C–G) whereas RNA is composed of only a single strand (runs in the 5'–3' direction) as shown in Figure 10.2.

To examine the genetic material of a cell, DNA must first be removed from the confines of the cell through the process of **DNA isolation**. This procedure involves dissolving the cell membrane and then removing proteins that are not part of the DNA structure. To break down the cell membrane (*i.e.* **lyse** the cell), the cells are subjected to some type of physical abrasion (*e.g.* vortexing, bead beating, etc.). Once lysed, a detergent, normally **sodium dodecylsulfate** (SDS), is added. The detergent functions to remove the lipids present in the cell membrane so that the DNA can be released into solution. In addition to the DNA, cellular proteins also present in solution need to be enzymatically digested with a protease enzyme such as Proteinase K. Following this step, addition of an alcohol (either isopropanol or ethanol) is required for precipitation of the

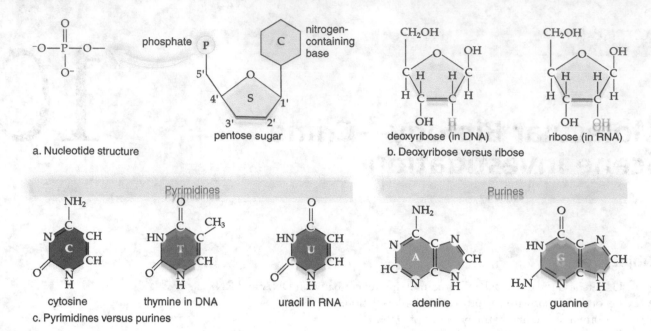

Figure 10.1

Nucleotide structural elements of DNA and RNA.

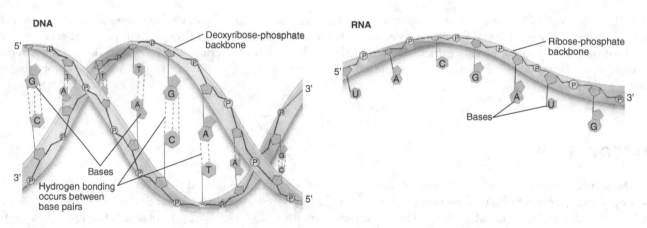

Figure 10.2

The structural composition of DNA and RNA molecules.

DNA out of solution. Finally, the DNA needs to be spooled and allowed to dry before dissolving in water and Tris-EDTA (TE) buffer.

In most cases, the quantity of DNA isolated from a sample is limited, especially when dealing with evidence (hair, blood, skin, etc.) collected from a crime scene. To have a sufficient amount for analysis, additional copies of the DNA need to be generated Copying of the DNA is achieved by the **Polymerase Chain Reaction** (PCR). During this process, a single piece of DNA, i.e. the template/target DNA, is amplified exponentially (1 copy → 2 copies → 4 copies → 8 copies → 16 copies, etc.) producing millions of copies.

Following PCR, the amplified products are separated by gel electrophoresis (Fig. 10.4). In this process, DNA, RNA or protein molecules are separated in a gel matrix based on size and charge. An electric current applied to gel creates a charge separation across the gel matrix, i.e. one side becomes positively charged (anode) and the other negatively charged (cathode). Because opposite charges attract, negatively charged molecules (e.g. DNA) move toward the anode, while the positively charged molecules (e.g. certain proteins) migrate toward the cathode. In addition, amplified products of smaller molecular weight have a tendency to move through the gel faster than larger products, which are retained near the wells (Fig. 10.5). Once electrophoresis is complete, the products/fragments can be visualized by a variety of methods including the use of ethidium bromide in conjunction with a UV irradiation system or simply by staining the gel with a safe stain (*e.g.* GelRed or QUIKView).

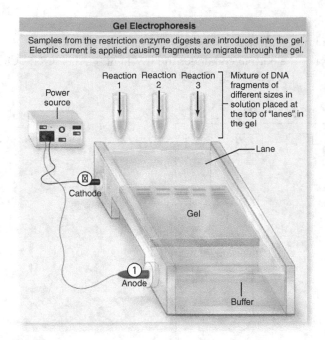

Gel Electrophoresis

Samples from the restriction enzyme digests are introduced into the gel. Electric current is applied causing fragments to migrate through the gel.

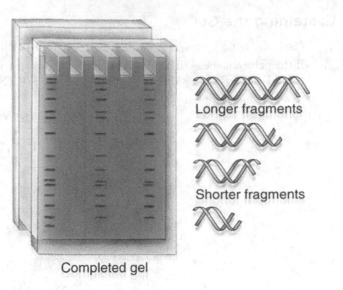

Longer fragments

Shorter fragments

Completed gel

Figure 10.4

End product of gel electrophoresis.

Figure 10.3

Laboratory set up for gel electrophoresis.

Task 1—GEL ELECTROPHORESIS

Procedure

A. Gel Preparation

1. Measure 2.1g of agarose in a weigh boat.
2. Pour the agarose into a 100mL flask.
3. To the same flask, add 70mL of 1X TAE electrophoresis buffer.
4. Try not to boil the solution. Heat the agarose-TAE mixture in the microwave for 1 min and then mix. Note: Always keep a close eye on the solution in the microwave. The timing could be off depending on the microwaves used.
5. Heat the mixture for an additional 1 min and then mix. The solution should be clear, not grainy. CAUTION: The flask will be very HOT! Use the autoclaves heat-protective gloves to handle the flask.
6. Add 4μL of Ethidium Brominde. CAUTION: EtBr is a carcinogen! Use Gloves!
7. Immediately pour the mixture into the gel cast. Add the appropriately sized well-making comb to the gel cast.
8. Allow the gel to polymerize for approximately 20 minutes.

B. Running the Gel

1. Once the gel has polymerized, remove it from the cast.
2. Transfer the gel into a 1X TAE buffer-filled electrophoresis box.
3. Using a micropipette, load your samples one at a time into each well. Use 10mL of each DNA sample per well. DO NOT RE-USE THE PIPETTE TIPES.

   Important Note: Change the pipette tip after loading each sample to prevent cross-contamination of the samples.
4. Once all samples have been loaded, replace the cover on the electrophoresis box, connect the cables from the power supply to the electrophoresis box and turn on the power source. Set the voltage to between 100 and 110 V.
5. **Before starting your power source make sure that the wells are on the cathode (–) end, not the anode (+) end.**
6. Allow the gel to run for approximately 30 min or until you see the bands about ¼ of the way from the end of the gel.
7. Turn off the power supply.

C. Staining the Gel

1. Carefully remove the gel from the electrophoresis box and transfer it to a UV Box.
2. If the gel so happens to be too thick, flip the gel over to view the bottom end under the UV light. CAUTION: YOU MUST WEAR GOGGLES TO VIEW THE RESULTS OF THE GEL ELECTROPHORESIS.
3. Sketch your results in the gel below.

L	CS	S1	S2	S3	S4
☐	☐	☐	☐	☐	☐

Questions

1. What does PCR allow you to do with DNA?

2. What components do you need to perform PCR?

3. What is the master mix and why do you need each component?

4. Why do you need to perform PCR on DNA evidence from a crime scene?

5. What steps make up a PCR cycle, and what happens at each step?

6. Why does DNA move through an agarose gel?

7. What is an Allele Ladder? What is its function in DNA profiling?

8. What is required to visualize DNA following electrophoresis?

9. Which of the profiles matches that of the DNA sampled from the crime scene?

10. What genotype is the sample collected from the crime scene?

11. Which suspects can be eliminated based on this analysis?

Task 2—FINGERPRINT EVIDENCE

The tips of our fingers are characterized by unique ridge patterns that develop before we are born. The primary purpose of these ridges is to provide friction to help grip objects. Every individual possesses a unique set of fingerprints, even identical twins. For this reason, fingerprints are used to identify individuals, associate them to objects they have touched, and even place them at a crime scene.

Fingerprints are classified into one of five categories: visible, plastic, latent, patent or exemplar prints. Visible prints are those that can be visualized with the naked eye and are usually formed when the fingerprint ridges are in contact with a colored material (e.g. paint, ink or blood), leaving behind a print on whatever surface is touched. Plastic prints are ridge impressions left behind in a soft substance such as soap or wax while latent prints are left behind on most objects that have been touched, but are invisible to the naked eye. Unlike visible and plastic print types, latent prints require the use of special tools for visualization. The most commonly used substance to detect this type of print is black powder, although other chemicals including iodine, ninhydrin, and superglue can be used.

Black powder, which is composed of charcoal or black carbon, is applied lightly to a nonabsorbent (e.g. glass, wood, tile or dried paint) surface using a camel-hair or fiberglass brush. The powder particles make the latent print visible by adhering to perspiration and body oils left behind by the fingers. Once visible, the fingerprints are scanned and uploaded into the Integrated Automated Fingerprint Identification System (IAFIS) database for comparison to the millions of fingerprint records already present. Exemplar prints are the prints collected purposefully from an individual. For instance, when criminal are arrested and taken to the police station the criminal's fingerprints are documented and put into a database. The print could be collected either on paper cards using ink or using a computerized scanning system. Patent prints are chance ridge impressions, which are visible to the human eye, imprinted on the surface of foreign material, like wet clay, flour, play-doh, thick grease etc. These prints are typically not lifted, instead they are recorded photographically or in some cases a cast could be made of the print.

Fingerprint Classification

The most commonly observed fingerprint type, with 60–65% of the general population bearing this pattern, is the loop fingerprint. To be classified as a loop, one or more ridges must enter from one side of the fingerprint before looping or curving around to exit from the **same** side. Each loop has one delta and one core. There are two major types of loop fingerprint patterns: Ulnar Loop and Radial Loop. To determine the difference between the two loop patterns you have to loop at the direction of the loop. If the loop pattern flow is on the same side as the pinky finger then it is an ulnar loop. If the loop pattern flow is on the same side as the thumb then it is a radial loop. The terms radial and ulnar are termed after the bones of the arm, ulna and radius.

A whorl pattern is exhibited by 30–35% of the general population. In this fingerprint class, the ridges are normally rounded and form a complete circle. All of the whorl fingerprint patterns will have 2 or more delta ridge pattern. There are four types of whorl fingerprints: Plain Whorl, Central Pocket Whorl, Double Loop Whorl and Accidental Whorl. The plain whorl is composed of ridges that complete a full circle with two delta ridge patterns on either side. The central pocket whorl makes a complete circle, but the circuit will look more elliptical than circular. The delta ridge is also typically more closely associated with the central circle in the central pocket than in the plain whorl print. Double loop whorl fingerprints are made up of two loops that circle around each other with two distinct cores. The final type, accidental whorls consist of print patterns that blend two of the fingerprint patterns together and typically have two or more delta ridge patterns that are closely associated with the central pattern.

The rarest of the three classes, being exhibited by only ~5% of the general population is the arch fingerprint pattern. As in the loop pattern, one or more ridges enter from one side of the fingerprint but instead of looping, the ridges arch before exiting from the opposite side of entry instead of exiting on the same side of origin. This fingerprint pattern typically does not have delta ridge patterns, except in the ulnar and radial arches. There are several types of arches Plain Arch, Ulnar Arch, Radial Arch and Tented Arch fingerprints. The plain arch has an even flow of ridges across the finger without any significantly defined wave of ridges upward. The ulnar arch has a delta pattern with ridges that slope towards the hand's pinky finger, while the ridges on a radial arch slope toward the thumb. The tented arch has a significant wave thrusting up at the middle of the print forming what literally looks like a tent.

Evidence collection

While wearing gloves, carefully pick up and wrap any solid object (e.g. glass, knife, hammer, etc.) present at the crime scene in a separate sheet of paper and package the items in a sturdy container to prevent breakage during transport to the crime lab. Dust each item collected for fingerprints, so that you can compare it to those collected from the 4 suspects and the victim.

Analysis

Before beginning this portion of your analysis, your instructor will demonstrate how to "lift" prints from the surface of an object for the entire class.

Procedure

1. Place a piece of paper towel on your lab bench and rest the object collected from the crime scene on top.
2. Using the fiberglass brush at your station, gently and lightly "float" some of the black powder onto the surface. Only a very small amount of the powder is required to make the print visible. When too much powder is added, it will fill in the spaces between the ridges, making the entire print dark and unclear.
3. Once the print is visible, gently dust the print in the direction of the ridges.
4. Use one of the clear flap lifters to lift the print off the surface. To do this, hold the clear portion of the lifter taut and press down on the base of the print first and then upward towards the top and beyond.
5. Staple each lifter in the space provided in the Prints collected section below. Examine each print(s) collected from the crime scene for the presence of loops, whorls or arches.
6. Compare your findings to the reference prints available at the front of the lab for V and S1–S4.

10–6

Prints Collected

Ridge Characteristics

One fingerprint may have more than 100 distinctly identifiable points of reference. When performing a criminal investigation one cannot solely rely on the general fingerprint category, although it would be helpful in narrowing down the potential suspects in the investigation. Fingerprint ridge characteristics must be identified to be able to properly identify a match between the fingerprint the individual it belongs to.

After identifying the fingerprint type from the collected evidence look at the fingerprint under the dissecting microscope and find identifying friction ridge marks. Draw these markings in the space provided below.

12. Which major fingerprint category do the prints found fall under?

13. Describe the fingerprint patterns observed of each print collected from the crime scene.

14. Based on the available reference prints, which profile, if any, matches the victim?

15. Which suspect(s) possess the same profile as those collected from the crime scene?

16. Which suspects can be eliminated based on this analysis?

17. Update your storyline in the space below. Did the fingerprint analysis influence your storyline? If so, explain how.

18. Can any suspect be eliminated at this point of the investigation? Who? Why?

Task 3—BLOOD IDENTIFICATION AND TYPING

A. Is it blood?

The most commonly used presumptive/preliminary test to detect the presence of blood is the Phenolphthalein assay, more commonly referred to as the Kastle-Meyer (KM) test. CSIs usually perform this test directly at the crime scene because its easy to use, highly selective and most importantly, the results are obtained almost instantaneously. This color-based assay relies on the Redox reaction of the phenolphthalein indicator with hydrogen peroxide and heme, the iron-containing portion of the hemoglobin molecule. It should be noted that this test is not confirmatory and that a positive result only indicates that the sample **may** be blood since vegetable peroxidases, household cleaners, bleach and salts also act as oxidants, giving a false positive result.

Analysis

1. Using the cotton swab collect a small sample of evidence for blood identification.
2. Apply 1–2 drops of alcohol onto the swab.
3. Apply 1–2 drops of the phenolphthalein solution onto the swab.
4. Wait a few seconds to look for the development of a pink color.
   - **Note:** If a pink color develops at this step, this is indicative of a false-positive.
5. If no pink color appears, apply 1–2 drops of Hydrogen Peroxide solution onto the swab or in the tube. At this point if you notice a large amount of bubbles this indicates a positive oxidation reaction. This would indicate a positive identification for blood.
   - **Note:** You will **NOT** use the blood collected for blood typing. Instead you will use vials of potential blood samples that have been previously collected from the crime scene for blood typing.

19. Record your observations in the space below.

20. How can you tell that oxidation occurred? What gas is being released?

21. Where were the samples found?

22. Update your storyline in the space below. Did the blood identification analysis influence your storyline? If so, explain how.

23. Can any suspect be eliminated at this point of the investigation? Who? Why?

B. What ABO blood group is it?

1. You will use each blood typing tray to determine the blood type of a particular individual.
2. Add 3 drops of CS blood to each well in the first blood typing tray.
3. Add 3 drops from the bottle labeled A antibodies to the well labeled A, 3 drops of B antibodies to the well labeled B and 3 drops of Rh antibodies to the well labeled Rh.
4. Mix each well with a toothpick. Make sure to use a different toothpick for each well.
5. After 1 min, examine the tray for agglutination.
6. Repeat steps 2–6 to determine the blood types of V and S1–S4.
7. Record your results in Table 10.1.

TABLE 10.1

Individual	Blood type	Rh (+/–)
CS		
V		
S1		
S2		
S3		
S4		

24. Update your storyline in the space below. Did the blood typing analysis influence your storyline? If so, explain how.

25. Can any suspect be eliminated at this point of the investigation? Who? Why?

Task 4—SPATTER ANALYSIS

Blood spatter analysis is a crucial piece of evidence in solving a crime since it allows the CSI to reconstruct the events that may have occurred during the commission of that crime. A thorough analysis of the blood's direction of travel, distance of travel as well as the angle of surface impact can give the CSI significant insight as to how the crime unfolded.

Blood spatter can be classified as **Transfer, Projected**, or **Passive** (Fig 10.5). The first spatter type, transfer, occurs when a wet, bloody surface, such as a hand, shoe, or even the murder weapon, comes into contact with another surface. Often times, a bloody fingerprint or shoeprint can be located and linked to a particular suspect.

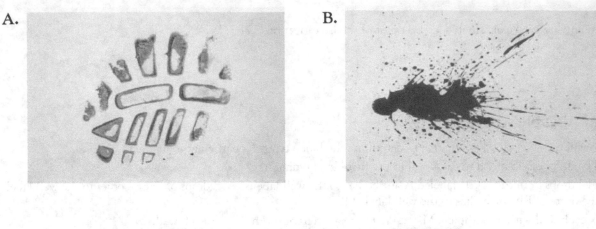

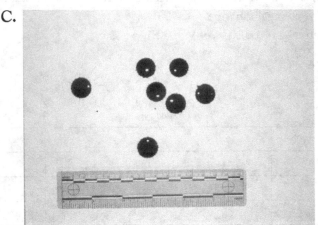

Figure 10.5

Types of blood spatter: A. transfer, B. projected and C. passive.

Projected blood stains, on the other hand, are created when an exposed blood source is subjected to an action or force greater than the force of gravity. The size, shape and number of stains are a direct result of the amount of force used to produce the spatter. For instance, in Figure 10.5B a projected pattern known as **arterial spurt** is illustrated. This pattern is commonly observed on a wall when an injury that occurred to the victim's neck results in a breached artery releasing blood with every heart beat. This second class also includes **impact spatter** which occurs as a direct consequence of a massive force or blow and results in the random dispersion of blood droplets. Impact spatter is further subdivided into three main types: **low, medium** and **high velocity** spatter. Figure 10.6A illustrates an example of low velocity spatter where the stains are typically ≥ 4mm and the force of impact is 5ft/sec or less. This type of spatter usually results after the victim sustains an injury, for example, blood drops resulting after being stabbed or hit with a hammer. In contrast, medium velocity spatters are typically ≤ 4mm in diameter and result form a force traveling anywhere from 5–100 ft/sec. A good example of this type of spatter is an intense beating with a fist or a bat (Fig 10.6B). The last type, high velocity spatter, results from forces traveling at speeds greater than 100ft/sec. The resulting blood drops are typically ≤ 1mm in diameter, usually appear as a fine mist or spray as shown in Fig 10.6C and are indicative of a gunshot wound(s).

The final category, passive blood spatter, consists of blood drops created or formed by the force of gravity alone. This type of spatter can be observed on any object or surface including carpets, tiles, tables and clothing. One of the most well known examples of passive spatter is blood dripping from a murder weapon (such as a knife, axe, etc.) or blood dripping directly from the victim.

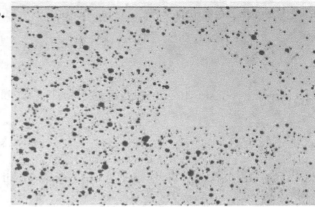

Figure 10.6

Types of impact spatter: A. low velocity, B. medium velocity and C. high velocity spatter.

Analysis

As you make your initial assessment of the crime scene, note the presence/absence of blood spatter. If present, determine the type of spatter and whether or not the spatter pattern corroborates the type of death suggested by the report. Record your findings in the space provided.

Sketch the blood spatter patterns in the space below:

26. For each blood spatter explain your reasoning for identification of the pattern and velocity of the spatter.

27. Update your storyline in the space below. Did the blood spatter analysis influence your storyline? If so, explain how.

28. Can any suspect be eliminated at this point of the investigation? Who? Why?

Task 5—HAIR EVIDENCE

When a crime is committed, hair is a common piece of evidence left behind. Forensic scientists utilize many of the characteristics intrinsic to hair as a means of linking a suspect to a particular crime scene. These properties include: resistance to chemical decomposition, maintenance of its structural features over long periods of time and most useful of all, the presence of DNA. It should be noted that, in addition to the aforementioned characteristics, hair present on different parts of the body possess disparate morphologies. Therefore, it is important to collect reference samples from the same origin of the body that the hair evidence is believed to have originated.

At present, one of the most commonly employed techniques for the examination of hair evidence is microscopy, although, with recent advances in technology, DNA typing is being performed as well. Even though microscopy cannot confirm that a hair sample originated from a particular individual, this technique can rule out potential suspects. Only when microscopy is used in conjunction with DNA analysis can the evidence sample be linked directly to a suspect.

Hair morphology

The structure of a hair can be compared to that of a lead pencil, with the cuticle represented as the outer yellow layer, the cortex as the wood interior, and the medulla as the lead in the center (Fig. 10.7).

1. **Cuticle** = outside covering of the hair shaft. This structure has a scaly appearance, with the scales oriented towards the tip of the hair. In humans, the cuticle's appearance is not sufficient for distinguishing between individuals. However, in instances where the hair has been chemically treated or dyed, the scales appear damaged and less flattened and may serve as means of differentiating between suspects.

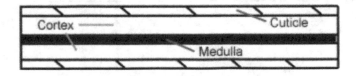

Figure 10.7

Basic structure of a hair follicle.

A.   B.   C.

Figure 10.8

Medulla classifications: A. continuous, B. interrupted and C. absent.

2. **Cortex** = the layer located immediately beneath the cuticle. The cortex is composed of cells and pigment granules thus it is responsible for hair color.

3. **Medulla** = the inner most layer of the hair shaft. The medulla's diameter is generally less than one third of that of the hair follicle, but this value varies between individuals. This layer is classified into one of three categories: (1) continuous, (2) interrupted, or (3) absent, as illustrated in Figure 10.8.

4. **Root** = the terminal end of the hair located within the hair follicle. It, along with the follicle, contains the cells necessary for hair growth. When pulled forcefully out of the head, the root may have a follicular tag which contains a rich source of DNA.

Evidence Collection

Wearing gloves and using sterilized tweezers/forceps collect 2–3 hairs from the crime scene. Place all hair samples in separate small manila evidence envelopes or pill boxes and seal the edges to prevent loss of the samples.

Analysis

1. Before beginning analysis of CS samples, examine the reference hair samples slides located in the slide box on your table.

2. Retrieve a single hair from the envelope of hairs collected from the crime scene and prepare a dry mount of the sample by placing it on a microscope slide and carefully positioning a coverslip on top.

3. Examine the dry mount microscopically beginning on the lowest magnification (4X) and increase the magnification accordingly until you can see enough detail.

4. Sketch your observations in the space provided below and label all visible components.

TABLE 10.2

Sample	Color	Thickness	Medulla Appearance	Cuticle Texture	Style
CS					
V					
S1					
S2					
S3					
S4					

Color: lt. brown, dk. brown, black, blonde, gray, etc.
Thickness: thin, thick, etc.
Medulla appearance: diameter, pattern (fragmented, continuous or absent).
Cuticle texture: rough, smooth, etc.
Style: curly, straight, frizzy, split ends.

29. Update your storyline in the space below. Did the hair evidence analysis influence your storyline? If so, explain how.

30. If the source(s) of the hair sample(s) collected from the crime scene cannot be determined, can any of the suspects be eliminated based on this analysis? If so, which one(s)?

Task 6—FIBER EVIDENCE

During the commission of a crime, fibers are frequently left behind through cross-transfer from the suspect to the victim and/or the surrounding area. This type of evidence is characteristic of incidents involving personal contact which include, but are not limited to, murder, battery and sexual assault. Once collected from the crime scene, the forensic scientist must first identify the type of fiber before attempting to link it to a particular suspect or distributor. Although a fiber sample can tie an individual to a crime scene, this type of evidence does not have significant evidentiary value because most fibers are not unique and therefore cannot definitively incriminate a suspect. In most cases, they are used as supporting evidence to strengthen the case against a particular suspect.

Fiber Types

1. **Natural Fibers** are those derived from animal or plant sources. Examples include cashmere, wool, fur, and cotton.
2. **Manufactured Fibers**, on the other hand, are derived from either natural or synthetic polymers. Examples include polyester, acrylic, rayon, spandex and nylon.

Evidence Collection

Wearing gloves and using sterilized tweezers/forceps collect 2–3 fibers of each type present at crime scene. Place each individual fiber type in a separate small evidence envelope to prevent cross contamination of the samples.

Analysis

1. Examine each fiber slide (cotton, nylon, wool, silk and rayon) available in the slide box at your station.
2. Examine each of the reference samples collected from the victim and 4 suspects.
3. Prepare a wet mount of the fiber(s) collected from the crime scene (CS).
4. Begin your examination on the lowest magnification (4X) and increase the magnification accordingly until you can see enough detail.
5. Record your findings and sketch your observations in the appropriate columns in Table 10.3.
6. Determine, if possible, the source(s) of the fiber sample(s) collected from the crime scene.

TABLE 10.3

Sample	Fiber Type	Color	Diameter	Striations (Y/N)	Particles (Y/N)	Drawing
CS						
V						
S1						
S2						
S3						
S4						

Burning Tests for Fibers

To confirm the fiber samples as a particular type of natural or synthetic fiber a flame test can be performed.

Procedure

1. Light the flame on the ethanol lamp or Bunsen burner.
2. Using forceps, hold the fiber close, but not in direct contact to the flame. Record your observations below.

10–14

3.   Using forceps, hold the fiber to the edge of the flame. Record your observations below.

4.   After using the defined samples use the crime scene sample to for fiber typing confirmation.

TABLE 10.4

Fiber	Results near the flame	Type of burning in flame	Results when removed from flame	Odor	Residue

31. Update your storyline in the space below. Did the fiber evidence analysis influence your storyline? If so, explain how.

32. Which suspect(s) was wearing the same type of fiber when arrested as those collected from the crime scene?

33. If the source(s) of the fiber sample(s) collected from the crime scene cannot be determined, can any of the suspects be eliminated based on this analysis? If so, which one(s)?

Task 7—CONCLUSIONS

The CSI needs an analyses report based on your findings. Since each investigative team focused on analyzing different types of evidence, your unit will need to combine its results to ensure that the evidence points to only one suspect. Record the results of all of your analyses in the following table.

34. Do all the pieces of evidence point to the same suspect? If not, which piece of evidence is contradictory?

35. Based on your unit's findings, which suspect is responsible for this horrendous crime?

TABLE 10.5

OVERALL FINDINGS FOR THE FIU CRIME SCENE UNIT

	CS samples	V	S1	S2	S3	S4
Hair						
Blood						
Rh						
Fingerprint						
Fiber						
Gel						

Evolution & Population Genetics

Objectives

- To gain a general understanding about the field of population genetics and how it can be used to study evolution and population dynamics.
- Understand the concepts of evolution, fitness, natural selection, genetic drift and mutations.
- To simulate Hardy-Weinberg equilibrium conditions.

INTRODUCTION

A **population** is a group of individuals (plant or animal) of one species that occupy a defined geographical area and share genes through interbreeding. Within a large population, new, genetically distinct subpopulations can arise through **isolation by distance (IBD)**. In this mechanism, as the subpopulations become geographically isolated, genetic differentiation between groups in the general population increases. These groups, more commonly referred to as **local populations** or **demes** (Figure 11.1), consist of members that are far likelier to breed with each other than with the remainder of the population. As such, their gene pool differs significantly from that of the general population and with continued isolation, demes may eventually evolve into new species.

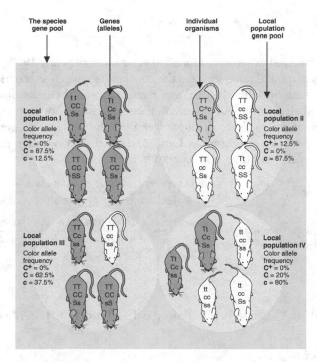

Figure 11.1

Local populations (demes) present within a large population.

Demes also arise from other mechanisms including geographical, ecological, temporal and/or behavioral isolation (Fig. 2).

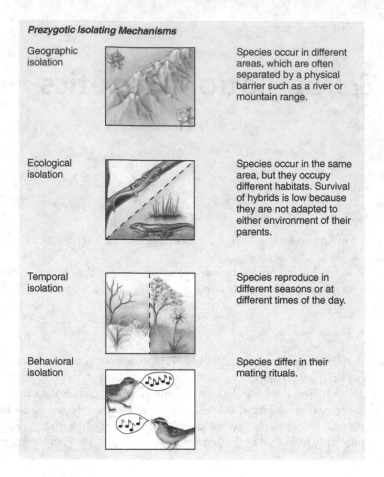

Prezygotic Isolating Mechanisms

Geographic isolation — Species occur in different areas, which are often separated by a physical barrier such as a river or mountain range.

Ecological isolation — Species occur in the same area, but they occupy different habitats. Survival of hybrids is low because they are not adapted to either environment of their parents.

Temporal isolation — Species reproduce in different seasons or at different times of the day.

Behavioral isolation — Species differ in their mating rituals.

Figure 11.2

Mechanisms of isolation.

Population genetics, which emerged as separate branch of genetics in the early 1900s, is a direct extension of Mendel's laws of inheritance, Darwin's ideas of natural selection, and the concepts of molecular genetics. The field of population genetics focuses on the population to which an individual belongs rather than on the individual. Within any given population, every individual has its own set of alleles; for diploid organisms, there are 2 alleles for each gene, one from the mother and one from the father. Collectively, every individual's set of alleles comprises the population's **gene pool**. The role of a population geneticist is to study the allelic and genotypic (Formulas **1** and **2**, respectively) variation present within a population's gene pool and to assess how this variation changes from one generation to the next.

$$Allelic\ frequency = \frac{\#\ of\ copies\ of\ an\ allele\ in\ a\ population}{Total\ \#\ of\ alleles\ for\ that\ gene\ in\ a\ population}$$

$$Genotypic\ frequency = \frac{\#\ of\ individuals\ with\ a\ particular\ genotype\ in\ a\ population}{Total\ \#\ of\ individuals\ in\ a\ population}$$

Example

In a population of 100 students, 64 are PTC tasters with genotype **TT**, 32 are PTC tasters with genotype **Tt** and the last 4 are non-tasters with genotype **tt**.

a.   **What is the allelic frequency t?**

$$\text{Allelic frequency of t} = \frac{2\,[\text{t allele in recessive genotype (tt)}] + \text{t allele in heterozygous genotype (Tt)}}{\text{Total \# of alleles for the PTC gene in the population*}}$$

*2 (# of alleles in homozygous dominant condition) + 2 (# of alleles in heterozygous condition)
+ 2 (# of alleles in homozygous recessive condition)

$$= \frac{2(4) + 32}{2(64) + 2(32) + 2(4)} = \frac{40}{200} = 0.2 \text{ or } 20\%$$

b.   **What is the genotypic frequency of tt?**

$$\text{Genotype frequency of tt} = \frac{\text{\# of tt individuals}}{\text{Total \# of individuals in the population}}$$

$$= \frac{4}{64 + 32 + 4} = \frac{4}{100} = 0.04 \text{ or } 4\%$$

In general, populations are dynamic units that change from one generation to the next. To be able to predict how a gene pool changes in response to fluctuations in size, geographic location and/or genetic composition, population geneticists have developed mathematical models that quantify these parameters. The most recognized of these is the **Hardy-Weinberg (HW) equation**, formulated by G. Hardy and W. Weinberg.

$$(p+q)^2 = 1 \text{ or } p^2 + 2pq + q^2 = 1$$

This equation relates allele and genotype frequencies in a population and indicates the proportion of each allele combination that *should* exist within a population. In this formula,

p^2 = the frequency of a homozygous dominant genotype (e.g. BB)
q^2 = the frequency of a recessive genotype (e.g. bb)
$2pq$ = the frequency of a heterozygote genotype (e.g. Bb)

The HW equation predicts **equilibrium**, i.e., the allelic and genotypic frequencies remain constant over the course of many generations, if the following five assumptions are met:

(1) Large population size,
(2) Random mating,
(3) No mutation,
(4) No migration,
(5) No natural selection.

In reality, no population ever satisfies HW equilibrium completely.

Example 1

If in a population of 100 cats, 84 carry a dominant allele for black coat (**B**) and 16 carry the recessive allele for white coat (**b**), then the frequency of the black phenotype is 0.84 and of the white phenotype is 0.16.

a.   Using the HW equation, calculate the frequencies of alleles **B** and **b**.

frequency of white (**bb**) cats = 16/100 = 0.16

q^2 = 0.16 therefore q = $\sqrt{0.16}$ = 0.4

since **p + q** =1, then **p = 1 – q**

therefore, **p** = 1 – 0.4 = 0.6

b.   Using the HW equation, calculate the frequencies of the **BB** and **Bb** genotypes.

From part a, we know that **p** = 0.6 and **q** = 0.4

therefore, the frequency of BB cats is p^2 = $(0.6)^2$ = 0.36

and the frequency of Bb cats = **2pq** = 2(0.6)(0.4) = 0.48

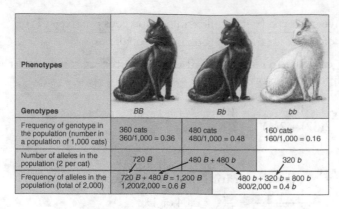

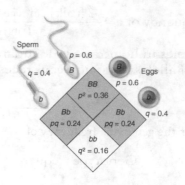

Phenotypes			
Genotypes	BB	Bb	bb
Frequency of genotype in the population (number in a population of 1,000 cats)	360 cats 360/1,000 = 0.36	480 cats 480/1,000 = 0.48	160 cats 160/1,000 = 0.16
Number of alleles in the population (2 per cat)	720 B	480 B + 480 b	320 b
Frequency of alleles in the population (total of 2,000)	720 B + 480 B = 1,200 B 1,200/2,000 = 0.6 B		480 b + 320 b = 800 b 800/2,000 = 0.4 b

Figure 11.3

Hardy-Weinberg Equilibrium Example.
To check: since $p^2 + 2pq + q^2 = 1$, then $0.36 + 0.48 + 0.16 = 1$

Example 2

In a population of fruit flies, the genotypes of individuals present are: 50 RR, 20 Rr and 30 rr where R = red eyes and r = white eyes. Assuming the population is in Hardy-Weinberg equilibrium, the proportion of each genotype would be determined as follows:

a. Using Formula 1, calculate the frequency of each allele, in this case R and r.

$$\text{Frequency of } r \text{ allele} = \frac{2[30] + 20}{2[50] + 2[20] + 2[30]} = \frac{80}{200} = 0.4$$

Therefore, **q**, the frequency of the recessive allele, equals 0.4.

b. Since q is known, the **p + q = 1** is equation is used to determine **p**, the frequency of the dominant allele.

$$\text{since } \mathbf{p + q = 1}, \text{ then } \mathbf{p = 1 - q}$$

$$\text{therefore, } \mathbf{p} = 1 - 0.4 = 0.6$$

c. Now using the HW equation, we can calculate the proportion of **RR**, **Rr** and **rr** individuals in the population.

From part a and b, we know that **p = 0.6** and **q = 0.4**

therefore, the frequency of RR individuals is $\mathbf{p^2} = (0.6)^2 = 0.36$

the frequency of those with the Rr genotype = $\mathbf{2pq} = 2(0.6)(0.4) = 0.48$ and the frequency of rr flies = $\mathbf{q^2} = (0.4)^2 = 0.16$

d. Since there are 100 flies in our population, when the population is in HW equilibrium, 36 flies are homozygous dominant (RR), 48 are heterozygous (Rr) and the remaining16 are homozygous recessive (rr).

The genetic composition of a population's gene pool can be affected by several evolutionary factors, including mutations, migration, non-random mating, genetic drift and natural selection. **Mutations**, changes in the DNA sequence, are the ultimate source of genetic variation in a population's gene pool but because mutation rates are generally low, mutations alone do not usually result in changes in allele frequency. Allelic distributions in a particular group can also fluctuate due to migration, i.e. the movement of individuals either into (**immigration**) or out of (**emigration**) a population, resulting in either the addition or loss of alleles, respectively. Diversity within a population is also affected by random events, a process referred to as **genetic drift**. Two examples of genetic drift are (1) **founder effects** (Fig. 3A) and (2) **genetic bottlenecks** (Fig. 3B). In the first scenario, a small group of individuals leave the original population and start a new population in a different location. In contrast, a bottleneck occurs when the original population is drastically reduced in size as a result of some type of natural disaster (e.g. fires, hurricanes, disease, etc.). In addition, **non-random mating** (e.g. inbreeding/self-fertilization—increases homozygosity) and **natural selection** (survival of the fittest) also alter the genetic variation within a population.

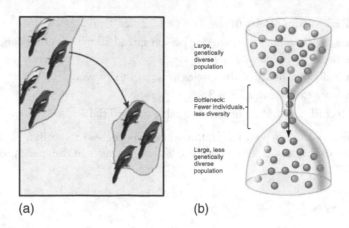

(a)   (b)

Figure 11. 4

A. Founder effect and B. Bottleneck effect.

In summary, the various techniques employed by population geneticists enable them to determine the frequency of gene interaction (gene flow) among different populations and examine the effects of natural selection, migration and mutations, on the genetic composition of these groups. Overall, population genetics attempts to explain how adaptation and speciation shape biological populations over time.

In today's lab you will use the concepts and techniques of population genetics to answer questions about the genetic composition of particular populations. Learning how gene flow occurs within and between populations can provide valuable insight about the processes that lead to genetic variation and ultimately speciation (i.e. evolution of new species).

Task 2—PEPPER MOTH: Industrial Melanism

Charles Darwin accumulated a tremendous collection of facts to support the theory of evolution by natural selection. One of his difficulties in demonstrating the theory, however, was the lack of an example of evolution over a short period of time, which could be observed as it was taking place in nature. Although Darwin was unaware of it, remarkable examples of evolution, which might have helped to persuade people of his theory, were in the countryside of his native England. One such example is the evolution of the peppered moth *Biston betularia*.

The economic changes known as the industrial revolution began in the middle of the eighteenth century. Since then, tons of soot have been deposited on the country side around industrial areas. The soot discolored and generally darkened the surfaces of trees and rocks. In 1848, a dark-colored moth was first recorded. Today, in some areas, 90% or more of the peppered moths are dark in color. More than 70 species of moth in England have undergone a change from light to dark. Similar observations have been made in other industrial nations, including the United States.

Industrial melanism is a term used to describe the adaptation of a population in response to pollution. One example of rapid industrial melanism occurred in populations of peppered moths in the area of Manchester, England from 1845 to 1890. Before the industrial revolution, the trunks of the trees in the forest around Manchester were light due to the presence of lichens. Most of the peppered moths in the area were light colored with dark spots. As the industrial revolution progressed, the tree trunks became covered with soot and turned dark. Over a period of 45 years, the dark variety of the peppered moth became more common. In general, birds in the area hunted the moths for food. The camouflage of the moths plays an important role in determining whether the birds could see and hunt their prey.

Procedure

1. Choose one person in the group to be the "bird predator".
2. Place a sheet of white paper on the table and have one person spread 30 white circles and 30 newspaper cutouts over the surface while the "predator" isn't looking.
3. The "predator" will then pick up as many of the circles as he can in 15 seconds.
4. Record your results in the data table under Trial 1.

5. Repeat steps 2–3 again. Record your results in the data table under Trial 2.
6. Place a sheet of newspaper on the table and have one person spread 30 white cutouts and 30 newspaper cutouts over the surface while the "predator" isn't looking.
7. The "predator" will then pick up as many of the circles as he can in 15 seconds.
8. Record your results in the data table under Trial 3.
9. Repeat steps 6–7 again. Record your results in the data table under Trial 4.

Based on what you know about the pepper moth, formulate hypotheses (Scientific, H_o and H_a) for what you expect to occur to the population numbers of the peppered moth. Write both hypotheses in the space provided and explain your reasoning for each.

Scientific:

H_o:

H_a:

MAKE PREDICTIONS

For each trial write down whether you expect the resulting number of white or dark peppered moths to have a larger population size or smaller population size than the other population.

TABLE 11.1

Trials	Population sizes (larger/smaller)
1	
2	
3	
4	

Results

Graph the class results using Excel. In the space below describe the trends seen on your graph.

TABLE 11.2

GROUP RESULTS

| Trial | Background | Starting Population | | Number Picked up | |
		Dark moths	White moths	White moths	Dark moth
1	white				
2	white				
3	newspaper				
4	newspaper				

TABLE 11.3
CLASS RESULTS

Trial	Background	Starting Population		Number Picked up	
		Dark moths	White moths	White moths	Dark moths
1	white				
2	white				
3	newspaper				
4	newspaper				

Questions

1. Which of the variables is (are) the independent variable(s)?

2. Which of the variables is (are) the dependent variable(s)?

3. What variables serve as controls and what do they control for?

4. Did your observed results reflect your predictions. Explain.

5. What did the experiment show about how prey are selected by predators?

6. Which colored moths are best adapted to an unpolluted environment? Use your results to support your answer.

7. Which colored moths are best adapted to a polluted environment? Use your results to support your answer.

8. What would you expect the next generation of moths to look like after Trial 1? Why do you think this?

9. What would you expect the next generation of moths to look like after Trial 3? Why do you think this?

10. What is natural selection? How your experiment show that natural selection occurred in the moth populations? Use your results to support your answer.

11. Do you reject or fail to reject your null hypothesis? Explain.

TASK 3—GENOTYPIC FREQUENCIES AND HARDY WEINBERG (HW) EQUILIBRIUM

You can use the HW equations and your knowledge about allelic and genotypic frequencies to address many population genetics questions. The four problems below provide excellent examples.

Questions

12. State the Hardy-Weinberg Equilibrium Equation and identify what each value in the equation means.

Problem 1: Gene and Genotype Frequencies

In addition to the ABO antigens, several other classes of glycoproteins are present on the surface of red blood cells. Examples include the MN, Rh, Duffy and Lewis antigens. For this exercise, we will focus on the MN blood protein system. The MN antigens, like the ABO blood proteins, display codominant inheritance where both alleles (i.e., M and N) are expressed simultaneously.

You are a member of a group of 100 students who have accidentally been locked in the gym overnight. To amuse yourselves, rather than playing "spin the bottle", "beer pong" or "truth-or-dare", you decide to calculate the frequencies of **MN** alleles amongst yourselves. Miraculously, everyone present knows his/her genotype. You learn that 49 people are **MM**, 42 people are **MN**, and 9 people are **NN**. If, **M** = **p** and **N** = **q**, answer the questions that follow, making sure to show all calculations:

13. How many **M** alleles are present among the group?

14. How many **N** alleles are present among the group?

15. What is the frequency of the **M** allele?

16. What is the frequency of the **N** allele?

17. What are the frequencies of **MM**, **MN** and **NN** genotypes?

Problem 2: Gene Frequencies in a Medical Application

The island of Madagascar has a total population of 1300 people, including 13 individuals who are afflicted by Cystic Fibrosis (CF), a recessively inherited disease. Researchers are interested in knowing how many people in the Madagascar populace are carriers of CF, and have requested your assistance as the resident physical anthropologist. If the **C** allele is dominant and the **C** allele is recessive, answer the questions that follow. (Show all calculations)

18. What is the frequency of recessive individuals in the Madagascar populace?

11–8

19. What is the frequency of dominant individuals in this population?

20. What is the frequency of the **Cc** genotype in Madagascar?

21. How many people in this population are normal (i.e. not carriers)?

22. How many people in this population are carriers?

Problem 3: Examine Your Own Traits

Using yourself and your lab mates, complete Tables 11.4, 11.5 and 11.6.

TABLE 11.4

INDIVIDUAL OBSERVATIONS

	Trait	Allele Character	Inheritance Pattern	Your Phenotype (check one)		Your possible genotype
DOM = dominant, REC = recessive				DOM	REC	
	Widow's Peak	W	dominant			
	Attached Earlobes	a	recessive			
	Darwin's Ear Point	E	dominant			

TABLE 11.4

INDIVIDUAL OBSERVATIONS

	Trait	Allele Character	Inheritance Pattern	Your Phenotype (check one)		Your possible genotype
DOM = dominant, REC = recessive				DOM	REC	
	Cleft Chin	c	recessive			
	Unpigmented Iris (blue)	b	recessive			
	Tongue Rolling	R	dominant			
	Tongue Rolling	f	recessive			
	Hitchhiker's Thumb	h	recessive			
	Freckles	L	dominant			

11–10

	Mid-Digital Hair	M	dominant			
	Dimples	D	dominant			
	PTC tasting	T	dominant			

TABLE 11.5

OBSERVATIONS FOR YOUR CLASS

Trait	Total Number	Number of Dominant Phenotypes	% of Total	Number of Recessive Phenotypes	% of Total
1. Widow's Peak					
2. Attached Earlobes					
3. Darwin's Ear Point					
4. Cleft Chin					
5. Unpigmented Iris					
6. Tongue Rolling					
7. Tongue Folding					
8. Hitchhiker's Thumb					
9. Freckles					
10. Mid-Digital Hair					
11. Dimples					
12. PTC tasting					

TABLE 11.6

EXPECTED ALLELE AND GENOTYPE FREQUENCIES* FOR YOUR CLASS

Trait	Allele Frequencies		Genotype Frequencies		
	p	q	p^2	$2pq$	q^2
1. Widow's Peak					
2. Attached Earlobes					
3. Darwin's Ear Point					
4. Cleft Chin					
5. Unpigmented Iris					
6. Tongue Rolling					
7. Tongue Folding					
8. Hitchhiker's Thumb					
9. Freckles					
10. Mid-Digital Hair					
11. Dimples					
12. PTC tasting					

*Note: these are the *expected* genotypic frequencies if the population is in HW equilibrium.

Task 4—MUTATIONS

In nature, mutation is the process that creates new alleles. Mutations are mistakes that happen during DNA replication before cell division, or abnormalities that develop in chromosomes during cell division. Whatever the source, mutations contribute to genetic variability in populations. However, their effect is usually much less than that of genetic recombination that occurs as a result of crossing over. Mutations can be neutral, having no effect, or be detrimental or even beneficial. Usually, but not always, mutations create recessive alleles. This means that the trait would not be expressed until it appeared in a homozygous individual, a process that could take several generations.

Natural selection is the agent in nature that determines whether a mutation is "good" or "bad." A detrimental mutation (allele) would be selected against; for example, organisms with the mutation would not function as well in the environment and would leave fewer offspring. Over time, the frequency of genotypes carrying a detrimental mutation should decrease in the population. The opposite would be true for a beneficial mutation.

In this task, you will experimentally induce mutations in two bacteria, *Escherichia coli* and *Serratia marcescens*. Bacteria are good organisms to use in mutation studies because they are haploid. If a mutation occurs, it is expressed because there is not a second allele present to mask it. You will study mutations affecting viability in these two bacteria. Such mutations are called lethal mutations because the mutant gene fails to produce a needed product and the cell dies.

Mutations can be induced by several means. Chemicals, called mutagens can change an organism's DNA, causing changes in hereditary information. Ultraviolet radiation has similar effects and will be used in the experiment, Because mutations caused by UV exposures are random, many different mutations will be induced in the bacteria. Some may affect pigment synthesis in *Serratia*. This bacterium is normally red, but when a mutation occurs in the genes producing the enzymes involved in pigment synthesis, no pigment is made and the bacteria are white. Other mutations will kill the bacteria because the UV exposure damages genes that are essential to life.

Based on what you know about UV exposure, formulate hypotheses (Scientific ,H_o and H_a) for what you expect to occur to the number of colonies at the different exposure times. Write the hypotheses in the space provided and explain your reasoning for each.

Scientific:

H$_o$:

H$_a$:

     Based on what you know about UV exposure, formulate hypotheses (Scientific, H$_o$ and H$_a$) for what you expect to occur to the number of *Serratia marcescens* colonies in comparison to the number of *Escherichia coli* colonies. Write the hypotheses in the space provided and explain your reasoning for each.

Scientific:

H$_o$:

H$_a$:

TABLE 11.7

PREDICTIONS

Exposure Time	Serratia marcescens	Escherichia coli
10 seconds		
30 seconds		
1 minute		
2 minutes		
3 minutes		
5 minutes		

MAKE PREDICTIONS

For each trial write down whether you expect the resulting bacterial populations to have a larger amount of colonies or smaller amount of colonies than the other bacterial population.

Procedure

1.   Using a plastic sterile loop pick up a very small amount of *E. coli* and place the bacteria into a test tube with 10 mL of LB nutrient broth. Allow the bacteria about 10 minutes to acclimate.
2.   Make sure that the bacteria is evenly distributed in the broth before performing the next step.
3.   Add 0.1 mL of the culture to 9.9 mL of LB Broth.
4.   Take 0.1 mL of the dilution culture and add it to 9.9 mL of LB Broth in the final test tube.
5.   Plate the volumes of bacteria according to Table 11.8.
6.   Repeat the steps for *S. marcescens*.
7.   Spread the bacteria on the plates using proper aseptic techniques.
8.   Expose the bacterial plates to UV light. Make sure the plates are dry before placing them open and upside down on the UV light box. WIPE DOWN THE BOX ONCE THE EXPERIMENT IS OVER.
9.   Follow the results tables to record your final results.

TABLE 11.8

EXPOSURE AND VOLUMES

Exposure Time	Sample Volume (μL)
0 seconds	10
10 seconds	20
30 seconds	20
1 minute	40
2 minutes	40
3 minutes	40
5 minutes	80

Questions

1. Which of the variables is (are) the independent variable(s)?

2. Which of the variables is (are) the dependent variable(s)?

3. What variables serve as controls and what do they control for?

TABLE 11.9

ESCHERICHIA COLI

Plate	Sample Vol.	Cumulative UV exposure (seconds)	Total No. Colonies	Colony adjustment factor	Corrected No. Colonies	% surviving
1	25	0		X4		
2	50	10		X2		
3	50	30		X2		
4	100	60				
5	100	120				
6	100	180				
7	200	300		X0.5		

Results

When you examine the plates, count the total number of colonies on each plate receiving short UV exposures received lesser volumes of the cell suspension, and the numbers should be corrected by multiplying the colony counts times a volume correction factor. This calculation makes all counts for all plates directly comparable. Record the corrected number of colonies for each treatment.

Calculate the percent surviving by dividing total colony count from plate #1 into colony counts for all other plates and multiplying by 100. Plot the percent surviving (from total counts) as a function of irradiation time.

3. Did your observed results reflect your predictions over time? Explain.

TABLE 11.10

SERRATIA MARCESCENS

Plate	Sample Vol.	Cumulative UV exposure (seconds)	Total No. Colonies	Colony adjustment factor	Corrected No. Colonies	% surviving
1	25	0		X4		
2	50	10		X2		
3	50	30		X2		
4	100	60				
5	100	120				
6	100	180				
7	200	300		X0.5		

4. Did your observed results reflect your predictions between the two bacteria? Explain.

5. Why is UV radiation effective in destroying most types of microorganisms?

TASK 5—RANDOM MATING, NATURAL SELECTION, MIGRATION, BOTTLENECKING AND MUTATION

This task will allow you to further examine the HW equilibrium model utilizing a set of cards representing alleles (**A**, **a**, and later on, **α**) and a number of given "events" that may affect the "gene pool." Half of the cards in the population have a lower case a on them and the other half have an upper case **A**. Distribute two cards to each student, with ¼ of the students receiving **AA**, ½ receiving **Aa** and the last ¼ receiving **aa**. In this task, each student will represent an insect that is part of a general population (i.e., the class) of insects. This particular insect species mates (randomly) once a year and then dies. Note that each year the number of offspring produced is the same as that of the previous year.

Note and record your genotype here: _____

Part 1: Random Mating

1. To simulate a random mating event, all students should now place their cards back into the "gene pool." Make sure to shake the "gene pool" occasionally to ensure randomness.
2. Each student should pick two cards from the "gene pool." The new allelic pairs chosen represent the second generation. Record the number and ratio of allelic pairs present in the new generation in Table 11.11.

TABLE 11.11

Genotype	Number	Ratio
AA		
Aa		
aa		
Total		

Questions

a. Is the ratio of genotypes from the second generation different from those in initial population?

b. Were either the first or second generations in Hardy Weinberg equilibrium? Why or why not?

c. What are the frequencies for the two alleles in each generation? Did they change? Why or why not?

d. What should happen if we create a third generation now, exactly as we did before? Would you expect changes to occur? Why or why not?

Part 2: Natural Selection

1. Each individual should exchange cards so that everyone returns to their initial genotype.
2. For this exercise, insects bearing the **aa** genotype are unable to get food and are highly susceptible to disease. As a result, half of the aa individuals are unable to mate. Your instructor will randomly select which of the **aa** individuals will not participate in mating and will instruct them to move away from the rest of the group.
3. All other individuals should place their cards back into the "gene pool" to represent random mating.
4. Following the mating event, each student should pick two cards from the "gene pool."
5. Record the number and ratio of allelic pairs present in the new population in Table 11.12.

How do you expect each of the genotypic frequencies to change as a result of this mating event?

TABLE 11.12

Genotype	Number	Ratio
AA		
Aa		
aa		
Total		

Questions

a. Did the ratios change from the parental population? Why or why not?

b. Did the number of alleles change? Why?

c. What would you expect to see over time, if this scenario keeps occurring to those with **aa**?

Part 3: Migration and Founder Effect

1. The individuals cast out of the breeding population in part 2 need to re-join the general population for this exercise.
2. All individuals should exchange cards so that everyone has the initial pair that he/she started with at the beginning of this task.
3. For this exercise, your instructor will choose every third individual to join a subgroup of the population that is going to migrate to a new location. These individuals should move to another section of the classroom to form a "New" population.
4. The remaining individuals, who form the "Homeland" population, should mate by placing their cards into the "gene pool." The migrated population should also mate by placing their cards into their own "gene pool."
5. After mating, each individual (in both populations) should choose two cards from their respective "gene pool."
6. Record the number and ratio of allelic pairs present in the new generation for both the "Homeland" and "New" populations in Tables 11.13 and 11.14, respectively.

How do you expect each of the genotypic frequencies of the "Homeland" and "New" populations to change as a result of this mating event?

What do you expect to happen to genetic diversity in the "New" population?

TABLE 11.13

"HOMELAND"

Genotype	Number	Ratio
AA		
Aa		
aa		
Total		

TABLE 11.14

"NEW"

Genotype	Number	Ratio
AA		
Aa		
aa		
Total		

Questions

a. Does the ratio of genotypes differ between these most recent generations and the initial parental generation? Why?

b. What about the allele frequencies? Why?

Part 4: Mutation

1   All individuals should exchange cards so that they have the initial pair that they started with at the beginning of the task.

2.   Your instructor will randomly choose three **A** individuals to undergo a mutation event of an **a** allele. These individuals should exchange cards with their instructor to represent this change.

3.   In addition, your instructor will also randomly choose three other individuals with an **A** allele to mutate of an α allele. These individuals should exchange cards with their instructor to represent this mutation event.

4   All cards should be placed into the "gene pool" to simulate random mating.

5.   At this point, each individual should pick two cards from the "gene pool".

6.   Record the number and ratio of allelic pairs present in the new generation in Table 11.15.

How do you expect the mutations to affect the resulting population? Explain.

TABLE 11.15

Genotype	Number	Ratio
AA		
Aa		
aa		
Aα		
aα		
αα		
Total		

Questions

a.   Did the ratio of genotypes change from the initial parental population? If so, why do you think this occurred?

b.   What about allelic frequencies? Why did this occur?

Significant Figures and Rounding

I

In the laboratory, students often ask how precise they should be in recording measurements during experiments. The question of precision also arises when doing laboratory calculations. A few simple explanations are given here to guide you in these quantitative aspects of laboratory biology.

WHAT ARE SIGNIFICANT FIGURES?

Significant figures are defined as *the necessary number of figures required to express the result of a measurement so that only the last digit in the number is in doubt.* For example, if you have a ruler that is calibrated only in centimeters and find that a pine needle is between 9 and 10 cm long, how do you record the length?

The definition of significant figures tells you that you should estimate the additional fraction of a centimeter in tenths of a centimeter and add it to 9 cm, thus indicating that the last digit is only an estimate. You would never write this additional fraction as hundredths or thousandths of a centimeter because it would imply a precision that did not exist in your measuring instrument.

However, suppose you have a ruler calibrated in millimeters and measure the same pine needle, finding that the needle is between 93 and 94 mm long. You should then estimate the additional fraction in tenths of a millimeter and add it to 93 mm which would be 9.3 cm plus the estimate.

Memorize and use this rule throughout the course: *When recording measurements, include all of the digits you are sure of plus an estimate to the nearest tenth of the next smaller digit.*

Doing Arithmetic with Significant Figures

Other rules apply to calculations. Several situations you will encounter are discussed in the following paragraphs.

When converting measurements from one set of units to another in the metric system, be sure not to introduce greater precision than exists in the original number. For example, if you have estimated that something is 4.3 cm long and wish to convert it to millimeters, the correct answer is 43 mm, not 43.0 mm because the number of centimeters was known only with precision to a tenth of a centimeter and not a hundredth of a centimeter as 43.0 mm implies.

When performing multiplication or division involving numbers with different levels of significant figures, recognize that the answer should be expressed only with the precision of the number in the calculation that shows the least number of significant figures. For example, if you wish to calculate the weight of 10.1 ml of water and you are told the density of water is 0.9976 g/ml, you would multiply the density times the volume to obtain the weight. However, the correct answer would be 10.1 g, not 10.07576 g. Because the water volume measurement is known only to three significant figures, the latter number conveys a precision that is not justified given the precision of the water volume measurement.

When performing additions or subtractions, the answer should contain no more decimal places than the number with the least number of digits following the decimal place. Thus, 7.2°C subtracted from 7.663°C yields a correct answer of 0.5°C not 0.463°C. If the first number had been known with a precision of 7.200°C, then the latter answer would have been correct.

WHAT IS ROUNDING?

The last example introduces the concept of rounding to the appropriate number of significant figures. The rules governing this are straightforward. You should not change the value of the last significant digit if the digit following it is less than five. Therefore, 3.449 would round off to 3.4 if two significant figures were required. If the value of the following number is greater than five, increase the last significant digit by one. Therefore, 88.643 would round off to 89 if two significant figures were required.

There is some disagreement among scientists and statisticians as to what to do when the following number is exactly five, as in 724.5, and three significant numbers are required. Some will always round the last significant figure up (in this case 725), but others claim that this will introduce a significant bias to the work. To eliminate this problem, they would flip a coin (or use another random event generator) every time exactly five is encountered, rounding up when heads was obtained and leaving the last significant digit unchanged when tails was obtained. Recognize, however, that if the number were 724.51 or greater, the last significant digit would always be rounded up to 725.

Examples of Rounding

49.5149 rounded to 5 significant figures is 49.515 ($= 4.9515 \times 10$)
49.5149 rounded to 4 significant figures is 49.51 ($= 4.951 \times 10$)
49.5149 rounded to 3 significant figures is 49.5 ($= 4.95 \times 10$)
49.5149 rounded to 2 significant figures is 50 ($= 5.0 \times 10$)
49.5149 rounded to 1 significant figure is 50 ($= 5 \times 10$)

II

Making Graphs

Graphs are used to summarize data—to show the relationship between two variables. Graphs are easier to remember than are numbers in a table and are used extensively in science. You should get in the habit of making graphs of experimental data, and you should be able to interpret graphs quickly to grasp a scientific principle.

In using this lab manual, you will be asked to make two kinds of graphs—line graphs and histograms. **Line graphs** show the relationship between two variables, such as amount of oxygen consumed by a tadpole over an extended period of time (**fig. A2.1**). **Histograms** are bar graphs and are usually used to represent frequency data, that is, data in which measurements are repeated and the counts are recorded, such as the values obtained when an object is weighed several times (**fig. A2.2**).

LINE GRAPHS

When you make line graphs, always follow these rules.

1. Decide which variable is the dependent variable and which is the independent variable. The **dependent variable** is the variable you know as a result of making experimental measurements. The **independent variable** is the information you know before you start the experiment. It does not change as a result of the dependent variable but changes independently of the other variable. In figure A2.1, time does not change as a result of oxygen consumption. Therefore, time is the independent variable and the amount of oxygen consumed (which is dependent on time) is the dependent variable.

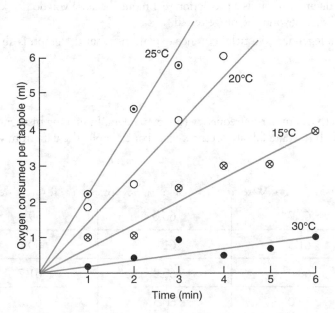

Figure A2.1
Oxygen consumption by a tadpole at four temperatures.

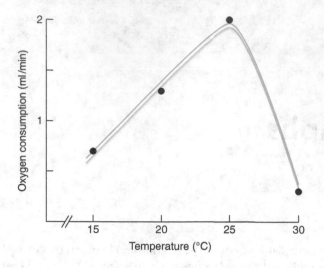

Figure A2.2

Derivative plot summarizes data from figure A2.1 and clearly shows how rate of oxygen consumption rises with temperature only to 25°C before declining.

2. Always place the independent variable on the x-axis (the horizontal one), and the dependent variable on the y-axis (the vertical one).

3. *Always label* the axes with a few words describing the variable, and *always put the units* of the variable in parentheses after the variable description (fig. A2.1).

4. Choose an appropriate *scale* for the dependent and independent variables so that the highest value of each will fit on the graph paper.

5. Plot the data set (the values of y for particular values of x). Make the plotted points dark enough to be seen. Always use pencil not pen in case you need to erase. If two or more data sets are to be plotted on the same coordinates, use different plotting symbols for each data set (·, ×, ⊙, ⊗, ⊡, etc.).

6. Draw *smooth curves* or *straight lines* to fit the values plotted for any one data set. **Do not connect the points** with short lines. A smooth curve through a set of points is a visual way of averaging out variability in data. Do not extrapolate beyond a data set unless you are using it as a prediction technique, because you do not know from your experiment whether the relationship holds beyond the range tested.

7. Every graph should have a legend, and a title sentence explaining what the graph is about.

HISTOGRAMS

Histograms are bar graphs that summarize frequency (or count) data. In making histograms, the count data are always on the y-axis. The categories in which the data fall are on the x-axis. For example, the data from which **figure A2.3** was drawn are as follows:

CLASS RESULTS FROM A SERIES OF WEIGHINGS OF THE SAME SAMPLE (IN GRAMS)				
61.0	60.0	60.0	59.8	58.0
61.5	61.5	61.0	60.9	58.0
59.0	60.0	60.2	61.7	60.6
59.7	59.0	60.3	63.0	60.4
62.0	59.0	60.7	58.5	59.0

Obviously there was variability in the data which should be summarized into a clear picture (fig. A2.3). To make a histogram, the x-axis was laid out with a range of 58 to 64 so that all values would be included. The values were then marked on the graph as lightly penciled Xs, one in each square of the graph paper for each observation. After all data were plotted, bars were then drawn to show the frequencies of measurements. On bar graphs, it is a good idea to show the average value across all measurements with an arrow. In calculating an average, remember the significant figure rule (appendix I).

A final about making graphs. Be neat! Remember most people do not trust sloppy work. Always print labels and use a sharp pencil, not a pen. Use a ruler to draw straight lines and a drafting template called a French curve to draw curved lines.

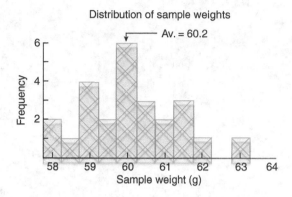

Figure A2.3

Histogram of a series of weights obtained by weighing the same sample several times. An average was calculated and is indicated by an arrow.

Simple Statistics

Quantitative data may be expressed in two forms, **count data** or **measurement data**. Count data are discontinuous variables that always consist of whole numbers. They are derived by counting how the results from an experiment fall into certain categories; for example, in a genetic cross between two heterozygotes, you expect to obtain a genotypic ratio of 1:2:1. Measurement data are continuous variables obtained by using some measuring instrument. The precision of the measurement depends on the fineness of the scale on the instrument; for example, a ruler calibrated in centimeters is not as precise as one calibrated in millimeters. Accuracy differs from precision in that it depends not on the scale used but on the calibration against a standard and the proper reading of the scale.

Whenever measurements are made, there are potential sources of error. Instruments and the humans who read them make random errors that affect accuracy. If the instrument is properly calibrated and if the person who is reading it is careful, the percent error is small and will be randomly distributed around the true measurement. If several readings are taken, the true value will be closer to the average of those repetitive measurements than to any single measurement.

In some cases, another source of error may be introduced. Bias occurs when an instrument is improperly calibrated or when the operator makes a consistent error in reading or sampling. For example, if a watch that is five minutes slow is used to measure the time of sunset for several days, the data will reflect a consistent bias, showing sunset as occurring five minutes earlier than it really did. Similarly, if a balance, spectrophotometer, or pipette is improperly calibrated, it will consistently yield a biased estimation either over or under the true value; and if the operator of the device misreads the instrument, additional bias enters. For example, if one looks at a car speedometer from the passenger's seat, the speed of the car appears to be lower than it actually is because of the viewing angle, called parallax. No statistical procedure can correct for bias; there is no substitute for proper calibration and care in making measurements.

Assuming that all sources of bias have been ruled out, there is still the problem of dealing with random fluctuations in measurement and in the properties (size, weight, color, and so on) of samples. In biological research, this is especially important since variation is the rule rather than the exception. For example, white pine needles are approximately 4 inches long at maturity, but in nature, the length of the needles varies due to genetic and environmental differences. A biologist must constantly be aware that biological variability and bias influence the results of experiments and any analysis should include procedures to minimize the effects.

Dealing With Measurement Data

When several measurements are made by an individual or by a class, most would agree that it is best to use the **mean** or **average** of those measurements to estimate the true value. However, determining the average alone may mean that important information concerning variability is ignored. Look at table 3.1, which contains two sets of data: the average temperature in degrees centigrade at 7:00 P.M. each day in September for two different geographic locations.

The average temperature for each location can be calculated by adding the readings for that location and dividing by the total number of readings:

$$\text{average temperature} = \frac{\sum \text{Readings}}{N}$$

where $\sum$ equals "sum of"

For both data sets, the averages are the same (15°C). Based on the averages alone, one might conclude that the two locations have similar climates. However, by simply scanning the table, one can see that location A has a more variable

TABLE 3.1

SEPTEMBER TEMPERATURES IN °C AT 7.00 P.M. FOR TWO LOCATIONS

Day	Location A	Location B
1	0	15
2	0	20
3	5	20
4	10	20
5	15	20
6	15	15
7	20	10
8	25	10
9	30	10
10	35	10
11	30	10
12	35	15
13	30	20
14	30	13
15	25	17
16	25	18
17	20	19
18	20	20
19	19	10
20	15	11
21	15	12
22	11	13
23	10	17
24	10	15
25	5	10
26	5	20
27	0	10
28	0	10
29	−5	20
30	−5	20

App. III–2

temperature than location B. Such temperature variations, especially those below 0°C, may have a tremendous effect on organisms; many plants and small insects may die at subzero temperatures. Therefore, reporting only the average temperature from this set of data does not convey crucial information on variability.

The **range** of values can convey some of this information. Location A had a mean temperature of 15°C with a range from –5 to 35, while location B's mean temperature was 15°C with a range of 10 to 20. Unfortunately, the range of values has a limited usefulness because it does not indicate how often a given temperature occurs. For example, if another location (location C) had 15 days at –5°C and 15 days at 35°C, it would have the same mean and range as location A, but the climate would be harsher.

To overcome some of the limitations of range, the data could be plotted in frequency histograms, with the x-axis showing the daily temperature and the y-axis showing the frequency of that temperature, or how often it occurs. The data for all three locations are plotted as histograms in **figure A3.1**. It is now obvious, looking at the plotted data, that these three locations have quite different climates even though the mean temperatures are the same and the ranges overlap for two of the three. However, this method of reporting is cumbersome.

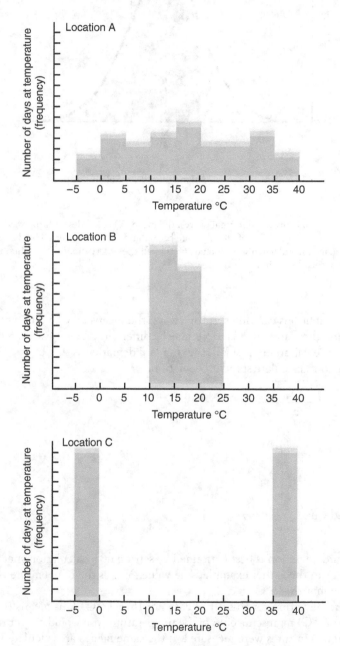

Figure A3.1

Frequency histograms of temperatures at three locations each having the same mean temperature of 15°C. Note differences in variation.

An efficient way to report information about variability and its frequency is to calculate the **standard deviation** from the mean. This value is calculated by determining the difference between each observation and the average. If a group of measurements is distributed randomly and symmetrically about the average, then the standard deviation defines a range of measurements in which 68% of the observed values fall. This is demon-strated in **figure A3.2.**

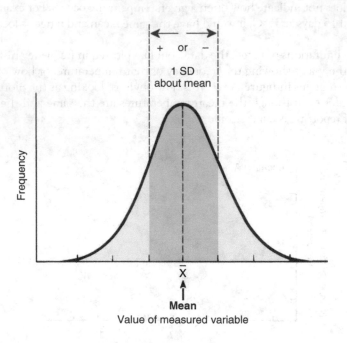

Figure A3.2

A frequency distribution representing a normal curve. On normal curves, the mean ($\bar{x}$) coincides with the mode, or the most frequently occurring value, and also with the median (the value at which 50% of all values are higher and 50% are lower). The dark shaded area corresponds to plus or minus one standard deviation about the mean, and will always include 68% of all the observations. The lighter shaded area is plus or minus two standard deviations and includes 95% of the observations.

Figure A3.3 shows that distributions can differ in threeways: the means may be different, the standard deviations may be different, or both the means and the standard deviations may be different. Obviously, when the standard deviation is large, the variability is great, and when the variability is small, the standard deviation is small.

The following formula is used to calculate standard deviation:

$$\text{standard deviation: } (\sigma) = \pm \sqrt{\frac{\Sigma(X_o - \bar{X})^2}{n-1}}$$

where

$\sqrt{}$ = square root
Σ = sum of
x_o = an observed value
$\bar{x}$ = average of all observed values
n = number of observed values

The computation of standard deviation is best performed by setting up a calculation sheet as in table 3.2. The numbers there are the ones from location A in the earlier example. The value for x_o is the temperature observation on each day, and $\bar{x}$ is the average temperature for the month, 15°C.

The mean and the standard deviation for this set of data are 15 ± 12°C. This means that the average temperature of 15°C plus or minus 12°C (3°C to 27°C) represents 68% of the temperatures you would expect to measure in this location during the same month that these tempera-tures were measured. If the same figures are calculated for the data set from location B, the results are 15 ± 4°C (not 4.2 because of significant figure rule; see appendix A). The mean and the standard deviation thus help convey an accurate impression of the similarities and differences between the two sets of data.

App. III–4

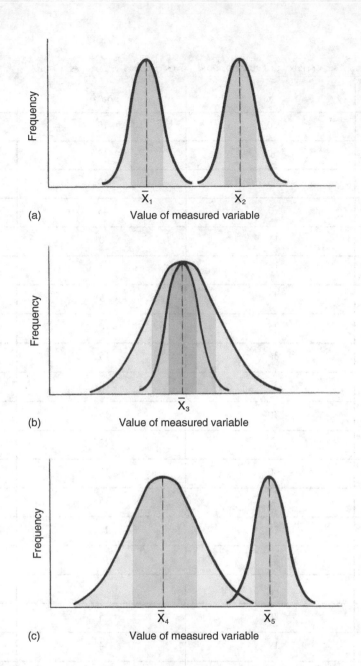

Figure A3.3

Three comparisons of normal curves that differ in their means and standard deviations. The dotted line represents the mean, and the shaded area represents plus or minus one standard deviation. In (a), the curves differ in their means but the standard deviations are the same. In (b), the means are the same but the standard deviations are different. In (c) both the means and standard deviations differ.

In teaching laboratories, each student usually makes only one or two measurements of a biological phenomenon. The concept of standard deviation is not appropriate for so few readings; a range and average are more suitable. However, if the class combines its readings so that there are 20 or 30 measurements, it is better to calculate the average and the standard deviation. Form the habit of reporting averages with some estimate of the variability when presenting data.

Comparing Count Data: Dealing with Variability

Often in experiments, theories are used to predict the results of experiments and data are recorded as counts or frequencies in categories. For example, Mendelian genetics can be used to predict the progeny from a cross between two heterozygotes. In cases where there is clear dominance and recessiveness, we would use our understanding of genetics to predict that offspring would occur in a ratio of 3:1. What happens when the actual results from a genetic cross of this type do not exactly fit the predictions? First, we

TABLE 3.2

CALCULATION SHEET FOR STANDARD DEVIATION USING LOCATION A DATA

n	X_0	$X_0 - \bar{X}$	$(X_0 - \bar{X})^2$
1	0	−15	225
2	0	−15	225
3	5	−10	100
4	10	−5	25
5	15	0	0
6	15	0	0
7	20	5	25
8	25	10	100
9	30	15	225
10	35	20	400
11	30	15	225
12	35	20	400
13	30	15	225
14	30	15	225
15	25	10	100
16	25	10	100
17	20	5	25
18	20	5	25
19	19	4	16
20	15	0	0
21	15	0	0
22	11	−4	16
23	10	−5	25
24	10	−5	25
25	5	−10	100
26	5	−10	100
27	0	−15	225
28	0	−15	225

App. III–6

29	−5	−20	0
30	−5	−20	400
0	$\Sigma = 450$		$\Sigma = 4182$

$$\bar{X} = \frac{\Sigma X_0}{n} = \frac{450}{30} = 15$$

$$SD \pm = \sqrt{\frac{4182}{30-1}} = \pm 12$$

would review the data for any obvious errors of technique or arithmetic and eliminate the data based on identified errors. If the data still do not conform exactly to our predictions, we must decide whether the variations are with in the range expected by chance.

When variations from the expected are small, we usually just round off and say that there is a good fit between the data and the expected. However, this is some what arbitrary and can become a problem as deviations from the expected become large. When are deviations no longer small and insignificant in comparison to the expected results (i.e., the theory is not a good predictor)?

Statisticians use a statistical test called the **chi-square(χ^2) goodness of fit test** to help them decide how much variation is acceptable. This test creates a number, the χ^2, which summarizes the differences between the data and what was expected. If that number is large, then the theory may be wrong. If it is small, the theory is a reasonable predictor of the results. The steps in using this test are outlined below.

Scientific Hypothesis

The χ^2 test is always used to test a hypothesis known as the **null hypothesis** (H_0). It is based on the scientific theory known as the model,which is the basis for predicting the results. A null hypothesis proposes that there is no difference between the results **actually obtained and** those **predicted** from a model within an acceptable range of variation.

A null hypothesis is paired with an **alternative hypothesis** (H_a), which proposes an alternative explanation of the results not based on the same scientific model as was the null hypothesis. The acronym "H_0H_a" emphasizes the coupling of hypotheses in statistical testing.

If a statistical test indicates that the results of an experiment do not fit the expected, then the null hypothesis must be rejected and the alternative hypothesis is true by inference: the data variation is greater than that expected by chance, and a factor other than that tested is influencing the results, implying that the model is not correct.

Rejection of H_0 does not prove H_a! This is a common mistake in the use of statistics. Rejection of H_0 only rejects the model on which H_0 is based.

Let us suppose that you are conducting breeding experiments. You are looking at a dihybrid cross involving dominant and recessive traits located on autosomes. Mendel's principle of independent assortment predicts offspring in the phenotypic ratio of 9:3:3:1. When the experiments were finished, the following results were obtained:

150 phenotypes dominant for both traits
60 phenotypes dominant for the first trait and recessive for the second
67 phenotypes recessive for the first trait and dominant for the second
23 phenotypes recessive for both traits

How would you determine whether these results were an acceptable variation from the expected 9:3:3:1 ratio? The actual ratio in this case is close to 7:3:3:1. Has the experiment failed to show Mendelian inheritance, or are the results simply within the limits of chance variability?

First, a null hypothesis should be formulated and then an alternative, mutually exclusive, hypothesis proposed. For the above experiment, these would be:

H_0: There is no significant difference between the results obtained and those predicted by the Mendelian principle of independent assortment.

H_a: Independent assortment does not predict the outcomes of this experiment.

Note how H_0 and H_a are mutually exclusive and both cannot be true.

Testing the Null Hypothesis

Because we are dealing with count (frequency) data, which should conform to those predicted by a model, the chi-square goodness of fit test can be used to compare the actual and predicted results.

First, a frequency table is created (table 3.3). The entries on the first line are the actual (observed) results from an experimental genetic cross in the lab. Those on the second line are the expected results obtained by multiplying the total by the fractions expected in each category ($9/16 \times 300$, $3/16 \times 300$, etc.).

The summary chi-square statistic is calculated using the following formula:

$$\chi^2 = \sum^n \frac{(O_i - E_i)^2}{E_i}$$

where

$\sum$ indicates "sum of"
O_i is the observed frequency in class i
E_i is the expected frequency in class i
n is the number of experimental classes (in this case 4)
χ^2 is the Greek letter *chi*, squared

It should be clear from inspecting this formula that the value of χ^2 will be 0 when there is perfect agreement between the observed and expected results, whereas the χ^2 value will be large when the difference between observed and expected results is large.

TABLE C.3

FREQUENCY TABLE OF OBSERVED AND EXPECTED RESULTS FROM HYPOTHETICAL FRUIT FLY CROSS

Day	Dom-Dom	Dom-Rec	Rec-Dom	Rec-Rec	Total
Observed (O)	150	60	67	23	300
Expected (E)	169	56	56	19	300

To calculate χ^2 for the data in table C.3, the following steps are required:

$$\chi^2 = \frac{(150 - 169)^2}{169} + \frac{(60 - 56)^2}{56}$$

$$+ \frac{(67 - 56)^2}{56} + \frac{(23 - 19)^2}{19}$$

$$= \frac{(-19)^2}{169} + \frac{(+4)^2}{56} + \frac{(+11)^2}{56} + \frac{(+4)^2}{19}$$

$$= 2.14 + 0.29 + 2.16 + 0.84$$

$$\chi^2 = 5.43$$

Therefore, for this experiment, the variability from the expected result is now summarized as a single number, $\chi^2 = 5.43$.

Making a Decision about the Null Hypothesis

To determine if a value of 5.43 is large and indicates poor agreement between the actual and predicted results, the calculated χ^2 value must be compared to a **critical χ^2 value** obtained from a table of standard critical values (table 3.4). These values represent acceptable levels of variability obtained in random experiments of similar design.

To use table 3.4, you must know a parameter called the **degrees of freedom (d.f.)** for the experiment; it is always numerically equal to one less than the number of classes in the outcomes from the experiment. In our example, the experiment yielded data in four classes. Therefore, the degrees of freedom would be 3.

In addition to knowing the degrees of freedom for an experiment, you must also decide on a **confidence level**, a percentage between 0 and 99.99, which indicates the confidence that you wish to have in making a decision to reject the null hypothesis. Most scientists use a 95% confidence level. Any other confidence level can be used and several (but not all) are given in table 3.4.

TABLE 3.4

CRITICAL VALUES FOR χ^2 AT DIFFERENT CONFIDENCE LEVELS AND DEGREES OF FREEDOM (D.F.)

d.f	Confidence Levels				
	$\chi^2.90$	$\chi^2.95$	$\chi^2.98$	$\chi^2.99$	$\chi^2.999$
1	2.7	3.8	5.4	6.6	10.8
2	4.6	6.0	7.8	9.2	13.8
3	6.3	7.8	9.8	11.3	16.3
4	7.8	9.5	11.7	13.3	18.5
5	9.2	11.1	13.4	15.1	20.5
6	10.6	12.6	15.0	16.8	22.5
7	12.0	14.1	16.6	18.5	24.3
8	13.4	15.5	18.2	20.1	26.1
9	14.7	16.9	19.7	21.7	27.9
10	16.0	18.3	21.2	23.2	29.6

If you now read table C.4 by looking across the row corresponding to 3 degrees of freedom to the column for 95% confidence, you see the value 7.8. This critical value means that 95% of the χ^2 values for experiments with 3 degrees of freedom in which the H_o is true fall below 7.8 due to chance variation and that only 5% will be above that value due to chance.

The next step is to compare the calculated χ^2 value to the critical value for χ^2. When this is done, two outcomes are possible:

1. The calculated value is less than or equal to the critical value. This means that the variation in the results is of the type expected by chance in 95% of the experiments of a similar design; the null hypothesis cannot be rejected.

2. The calculated χ^2 value is greater than the critical value. This means that results would occur only 5% of the time by chance. Stated another way, these results should not be accepted as fitting the model; the null hypothesis should be rejected.

When these decision-making rules are applied to our calculated χ^2 value, 5.43 is obviously less than 7.8. Therefore, although our ratio was not 9:3:3:1, it is within an acceptable limit of variation and we cannot reject the H_o. A model based on the Mendelian principle of independent assortment predicts the results of the experiment. Note, however, that you have not proven your H_o; you simply failed to reject it with 95% confidence in your decision. This is more than a subtle difference because it indicates that scientific knowledge is probabilistic and not absolute.

A Hypothetical Alternative

For illustration, let us suppose that another group got different results. When they calculated their χ^2 value, it was 9.4. If they went through the same decision-making steps that we just did, they would reject the null hypothesis: Mendelian genetics did not have predictive power for their experiment. In rejecting the null hypothesis, they can have 95% confidence that they are not making a mistake by rejecting what is actually a true null hypothesis.

Those who have studied table 3.4 might suggest a change in strategy here. If this second group changed its confidence level to 97.5%, the critical value becomes 9.8, which is greater than the calculated value of 9.4, thus keeping the group from rejecting the null hypothesis. This illustrates that by choosing a higher value for a confidence level at a constant number of degrees of freedom, the critical value will be larger, allowing one to accept almost any null hypothesis. Is this not arbitrary, the very situation we sought to avoid by invoking this statistical test?

The solution to this dilemma is found in what is really tested by the chi-square goodness of fit test. The comparison of calculated and critical χ^2 values is done to attempt to falsify the H_o, to reject it at a predetermined confidence level. If H_o cannot be rejected, then by default it is accepted. *You have not proven H_o, you have simply failed to disprove it.* The confidence level that is stated before each test represents the confidence you have in rejecting the null hypothesis, not the confidence you have in accepting it. As you increase the confidence level, you decrease the likelihood of rejecting H_o.

Statisticians often speak of type I and type II errors in statistical testing. A **type I error** is the probability that you will reject a true null hypothesis. A **type II error** is the probability that you will accept a false null hypothesis. As you increase the confidence level, you reduce the probability that you will reject a true null hypothesis (type I error), but you increase the probability that you will accept a false one (type II error). The confidence level of 95% is used by convention because it represents a compromise between the probabilities of making type I versus type II errors. The basis of this conservatism in science is the recognition that it is better to reject a true hypothesis than it is to accept a false one. Once a confidence level is stated for an experiment, it should not be changed according to the whim of the experimenter who wants a model to have predictive power. Those who change the confidence level run the risk of accepting fiction as fact.

Credits

All photos and line art not mentioned here are courtesy of the authors, Kristy Calero, and Jose Alberte.

Photo Log

Figure 2.1: © Dr. William Heidcamp; 2.8a: © The Print Collector/Alamy; 2.8b: © Biophoto Associates/Photo Researchers; 2.9b: © Ralph A. Slepecky/Visuals Unlimited; 3.8a–c: © David M. Phillips/Visuals Unlimited; 6.3 (all): © Ed Reschke; 7.6a: © The McGraw-Hill Companies, Inc./Joe DeGrandis, photographer; 7.6b: © The Mcgraw-Hill Companies, Inc./Ken Karp, photographer; 7.8: © Andy Jackson/Alamy; 8.5: © Jeremy Burgess/Photo Researchers, Inc.; 10.5–10.6: © Kevin Maloney and FORident Software; 11.4a: © Lars A. Niki; 11.4b: © The Mcgraw-Hill Companies, Inc./Ken Karp, photographer; 11.4c: © The McGraw-Hill Companies, Inc./Joe DeGrandis, photographer; 11.4d: © Steven Schleuning; 11.4e: © Digital Vision/Getty Images; 11.4f: © JupiterImages/Comstock/Getty Images; 11.4g: © McGraw-Hill Companies, Inc/Ken Carp, photographer; 11.4h: © 2012 Juan Naharro Gimenez/Getty Images; 11.4i: © Stockbyte/Getty Images; 11.4j: © GoodShoot/Picture Quest; 11.4l: © Rubberball; 11.4m: Courtesy of Ginsberg Scientific

Line Art Log

Figure 1, 2.5: Warren Dolphin, *Biological Investigations Lab Manual*, 8e © 2008 reproduced with permission of the McGraw-Hill Companies, Inc.

Figure 2.8b: Marjorie Kelly Cowan, *Microbiology: A Systems Approach*, 3e © 2012 reproduced with permission of the McGraw-Hill Companies, Inc.

Figure 2.9a, 8.1, 10.1: Sylvia Mader, *Biology*, 9e © 2007 reproduced with permission of the McGraw-Hill Companies, Inc.

Figure 2.10: Sylvia Mader, *Human Biology*, 12e © 2012 reproduced with permission of the McGraw-Hill Companies, Inc.

Figure 2.11a, 2.12–3.5, 3.8, 4.2, 5.1a–5.7, 6.1, 6.2, 8.2, 8.10: Peter Raven, *Biology*, 9e © 2011 reproduced with permission of the McGraw-Hill Companies, Inc.

Figure 2.11b: Darrell Vodopich, *Biology Lab Manual*, 8e © 2008 reproduced with permission of the McGraw-Hill Companies, Inc.

Figure 3.7, 10.4, 11.1: Eldon Enger, *Concepts in Biology*, 12e © 2007 reproduced with permission of the McGraw-Hill Companies, Inc.

Figure 4.1: Joelle Presson, *Biology: Dimensions of Life*, © 2008 reproduced with permission of the McGraw-Hill Companies, Inc.

Figure 4.2, 6.3, 6.4, 7.1, 7.2: Stuart Fox, *Human Physiology*, 11e © 2009 reproduced with permission of the McGraw-Hill Companies, Inc.

Figure 4.4, 8.3, 10.3: Peter Raven, *Biology*, 8e © 2008 reproduced with permission of the McGraw-Hill Companies, Inc.